WIND-DRIVEN OCEAN CIRCULATION

Gordon J. F. MacDonald, University of California at Los Angeles
Consulting Editor

Wind-Driven Ocean Circulation is one of a special series of brief books covering selected topics in the pure and applied sciences.

Wind-Driven Ocean Circulation

A Collection of Theoretical Studies

EDITED BY

Allan R. Robinson

Blaisdell Publishing Company
New York, Toronto, London
A Division of Random House

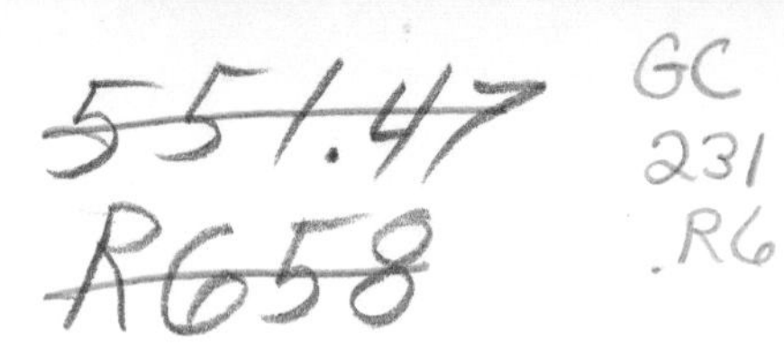

First Edition, 1963

Published in New York, Toronto, and London by Blaisdell Publishing Company. Distributed in Canada by Random House of Canada, Limited, Toronto.

Library of Congress Catalog Card Number: 63–8926

Manufactured in the United States of America

Preface

The papers collected in this volume are concerned with one particular aspect of the problem of the general circulation of the oceans: the relation of the permanent features of the horizontal circulation patterns to the distribution of mean atmospheric winds. Although these papers do not form an historical or classical collection, in the opinion of the editor, a study of them can provide the reader with a good first-hand knowledge of the present state of the subject. General circulation theory is evolving. *Per se*, these papers constitute fascinating studies of bounded flow in a rotating fluid of enormous Reynolds number. The application of these idealized mathematical studies to the circulation of real oceans lies in their use as separate pieces of an heuristic jig-saw puzzle. It is hoped that the thoughtful reader will discover something of what is unknown as well as known about the oceans.

The first two papers, those of Sverdrup (1947) and Stommel (1948), are fundamental to those which ensue. Sverdrup demonstrates how an almost geostrophic flow over the major part of the oceans can balance locally the stresses imposed by the wind, but that such a flow cannot describe a closed circulation pattern. The latitudinal variation of the vertical component of the earth's rotation vector is essential. That local regions of high relative vorticity must be present to complete the flow was recognized by Stommel; the underlying cause of the Gulf Stream was thus first exposed. An editor's introduction to the remaining papers may be found in sections 1 and 2 of the paper by Carrier and Robinson (1962). Further remarks have been reserved for Editor's Notes at the end of the book since a familiarity with the papers is assumed.

The kind cooperation of the authors and the journals of original publication is gratefully acknowledged.

Harvard University
May 25, 1962

A. R. Robinson

Contents

WIND-DRIVEN OCEAN CIRCULATION

Wind-driven currents in a baroclinic ocean; with application to the equatorial currents of the eastern Pacific

H. U. Sverdrup

Reprinted with permission from
Proceedings of the National Academy of Sciences
Volume 33, Number 11,
pages 318 through 326, 1947

*WIND-DRIVEN CURRENTS IN A BAROCLINIC OCEAN; WITH APPLICATION TO THE EQUATORIAL CURRENTS OF THE EASTERN PACIFIC**

By H. U. Sverdrup

Scripps Institution of Oceanography, University of California, La Jolla, California

Communicated July 31, 1947

1. *Introduction.*—Permanent ocean currents are computed from the observed distribution of density on the assumptions (1) that the horizontal pressure gradient is balanced by the Coriolis force (the deflecting force of the earth's rotation) and (2) that the horizontal velocities and the horizontal pressure gradient vanish at a moderate depth below the sea surface. The second condition can be fulfilled only in a baroclinic system, that is, in a system in which the isosteric surfaces intersect the isobaric surfaces.

In the computation of currents acceleration and frictional forces are neglected. Experience indicates that the computations lead to nearly correct results, implying that accelerations and frictional forces are small, but since friction is not entirely lacking, energy must be supplied to the ocean in order to maintain the permanent currents and the corresponding permanent distribution of mass. This energy can be supplied by the effects of heating and cooling or by the stress which the prevailing winds exert on the sea surface. Of the sources the latter is generally considered to be the more important. We shall examine effects of the wind stress only, taking into account that the ocean waters in motion represent a baroclinic system.

Ekman[1] and Stockmann[2] have examined the currents which develop in a *homogeneous* ocean under the influence of a stress exerted on the free surface, and Fjeldstad[3] has solved a special problem dealing with baroclinic conditions. If the general problem for a baroclinic ocean could be solved, knowledge of the wind stress alone would enable us to compute the permanent ocean currents, provided the effects of heating and cooling were negligible. A treatment of this general problem would present great mathematical difficulties because it would require the introduction of lateral frictional stresses and complete boundary conditions. Here we shall deal with the special case of equatorial currents in a region where lateral stresses can be neglected, boundary conditions are relatively simple, wind systems are semipermanent, and where our results imply that effects of heating and cooling, if present, need not be considered explicitly.

The striking feature of the currents of the equatorial regions is that imbedded between the currents which flow toward the *west* under the influence of the prevailing trade winds equatorial counter currents flow toward the *east*. In the Pacific and Atlantic Oceans the counter current is particularly well developed in the eastern parts of the oceans where it is located north of the equator, its axis coinciding approximately with the location of the equatorial calm belt which is found further to the north in summer than in winter. In the Indian Ocean the counter current is found to the south of the equator, but in the northern winter only.

Our specific problem is to determine whether the equatorial currents, including the counter currents, can be accounted for on the basis of our knowledge of the wind stress only. This problem was first approached by Montgomery and Palmén,[4] but Stockmann[2] has shown that they did not treat it in a sufficiently general manner. Stockmann's theoretical results, however, are not applicable to the conditions in the ocean because he assumed homogeneous water, but a similar analysis for a baroclinic system leads to a remarkable agreement between theoretical conclusions and observed conditions.

2. Theory.—The ocean waters are so nearly in hydrostatic equilibrium that at any depth the pressure, p, can be determined by a numerical integration of the hydrostatic equation:

$$dp = g\rho \, dz \tag{1}$$

provided that the density, ρ, is known from observations. In equation (1) and in the following equations the z-axis is positive downwards.

Neglecting lateral stresses the equations of horizontal motion can be written:

$$\begin{aligned} \frac{\partial u}{\partial t} + u\frac{\partial u}{\partial x} + v\frac{\partial u}{\partial y} &= -\frac{1}{\rho}\frac{\partial p}{\partial x} + \lambda v + \frac{1}{\rho}\frac{\partial}{\partial z}\left(A\frac{\partial u}{\partial z}\right) \\ \frac{\partial v}{\partial t} + u\frac{\partial v}{\partial x} + v\frac{\partial v}{\partial y} &= -\frac{1}{\rho}\frac{\partial p}{\partial y} - \lambda u + \frac{1}{\rho}\frac{\partial}{\partial z}\left(A\frac{\partial v}{\partial z}\right) \end{aligned} \tag{2}$$

where u and v are the horizontal velocity components in a rectilinear coordinate system, $\lambda = 2\omega \sin \varphi$ (ω the earth's angular velocity of rotation, φ the latitude, taken positive to the north of the equator), and A is the eddy viscosity.

We shall assume stationary conditions,

$$\frac{\partial u}{\partial t} = \frac{\partial v}{\partial t} = 0, \tag{3}$$

and shall neglect the non-linear terms, the field accelerations:

$$u\frac{\partial u}{\partial x} + v\frac{\partial u}{\partial y} = u\frac{\partial v}{\partial x} + v\frac{\partial v}{\partial y} = 0, \tag{4}$$

thereby placing severe restrictions upon the possible lateral boundary conditions. Equations (2) reduce to:

$$\frac{\partial p}{\partial x} = \lambda\rho v + \frac{\partial}{\partial z}\left(A\frac{\partial u}{\partial z}\right)$$
$$\frac{\partial p}{\partial y} = -\lambda\rho u + \frac{\partial}{\partial z}\left(A\frac{\partial v}{\partial z}\right) \tag{5}$$

stating that the horizontal pressure gradient is balanced by the Coriolis force and frictional stresses exerted on horizontal surfaces. In *homogeneous* water the horizontal pressure gradient is independent of depth but in a *baroclinic* system varies with depth. In the ocean it generally vanishes at a moderate depth, less than that to the bottom. We define a function P by the integrals

$$\frac{\partial P}{\partial x} = \int_0^d \frac{\partial p}{\partial x}dz, \qquad \frac{\partial P}{\partial y} = \int_0^d \frac{\partial p}{\partial y}dz \tag{6}$$

where d is equal to or greater than the depth at which the horizontal pressure gradient becomes zero. The function P, which is closely related to the P-function introduced by Ekman,[5] can be computed from the observed vertical distribution of density at a single oceanographic station, using equation (1).

The horizontal velocity must vanish at or above the depth d. The integrals

$$M_x = \int_0^d \rho\, u dz, \qquad M_y = \int_0^d \rho\, v dz \tag{7}$$

represent therefore the components of the *net* mass transport by the currents.

Integrating equations (5) from 0 to d, and introducing the horizontal boundary conditions:

$$\left(A\frac{\partial u}{\partial z}\right)_0 = -\tau_x, \qquad \left(A\frac{\partial u}{\partial z}\right)_d = 0$$
$$\left(A\frac{\partial v}{\partial z}\right)_0 = -\tau_y, \qquad \left(A\frac{\partial v}{\partial z}\right)_d = 0 \tag{8}$$

where τ_x and τ_y are the components of the wind stress, we obtain:

$$\frac{\partial P}{\partial x} = \lambda M_y + \tau_x \tag{9a}$$

$$\frac{\partial P}{\partial y} = -\lambda M_x + \tau_y \tag{9b}$$

The terms in equations (9) are well known in oceanography. Omitting the stress components the equations give the mass transport related to the distribution of density, or assuming homogeneous water in hydrostatic equilibrium ($\partial P/\partial x = \partial P/\partial y = 0$) they give the mass transport by pure wind currents. Equations (9) have been used by Defant[6] for computing the wind stress from oceanographic observations, including direct measurements of currents, but they have not been applied to other problems.

For application to other problems we add the equation:

$$\frac{\partial M_x}{\partial x} + \frac{\partial M_y}{\partial y} = 0 \tag{10}$$

which is obtained by integration of the equation of continuity, assuming that the vertical velocity is zero at the free surface and at the depth d. The three equations (9a), (9b) and (10) can be considered as relating the three unknown quantities, P, M_x, and M_y, to the known wind stress. Consequently, the distribution of density, as described by the partial derivatives of P, and the mass transport by the corresponding currents can be expressed as functions of the stress.

In applying equations (9) and (10) to equatorial currents we place the positive x-axis toward the east and the positive y-axis toward the north, and let $y = 0$ at the equator ($\varphi = 0$). Since

$$dy = R\,d\varphi \tag{11}$$

where R is the radius of the earth:

$$\frac{\partial \lambda}{\partial x} = 0, \qquad \frac{\partial \lambda}{\partial y} = \frac{2\omega \cos \varphi}{R}, \qquad \frac{\partial^2 \lambda}{\partial y^2} = -\frac{2\omega \sin \varphi}{R^2} \tag{12}$$

Differentiating equation (9a) with respect to y and (9b) with respect to x, subtracting and taking equations (10) and (12) into account, we obtain

$$M_y \frac{\partial \lambda}{\partial y} + \left(\frac{\partial \tau_x}{\partial y} - \frac{\partial \tau_y}{\partial x}\right) = 0 \tag{13}$$

In the trade-wind belt of the eastern Pacific the term $\partial \tau_y/\partial x$ is so small that with good approximation:

$$M_y = \frac{\partial \tau_x}{\partial y} \Big/ \frac{\partial \lambda}{\partial y} = -\frac{\partial \tau_x}{\partial y} \frac{R}{2\omega \cos \varphi} \tag{14}$$

Introducing equation (14) in (9a):

$$\frac{\partial P}{\partial x} = -\frac{\partial \tau_x}{\partial y} R \tan \varphi + \tau_x \tag{15}$$

or, writing differences on the left-hand side:

$$\frac{\Delta P}{\Delta x} = -\frac{\overline{\partial \tau_x}}{\partial y} R \tan \varphi + \bar{\tau}_x \tag{16}$$

where averages over the distance Δx are indicated by bars.

From equations (10) and (14) follows

$$\frac{\partial M_x}{\partial x} = \frac{1}{2\omega \cos \varphi} \left(\frac{\partial \tau_x}{\partial y} \tan \varphi + \frac{\partial^2 \tau_x}{\partial y^2} R \right) \tag{17}$$

When integrating equation (17) from 0 to Δx we shall assume a north-south vertical boundary at $x = 0$ at which the kinematic boundary condition $u_0 = 0$ must be satisfied in the form $M_6 = 0$. We obtain:

$$M_x = \frac{\Delta x}{2\omega \cos \varphi} \left(\frac{\overline{\partial \tau_x}}{\partial y} \tan \varphi + \frac{\overline{\partial^2 \tau_x}}{\partial y^2} R \right) \tag{18}$$

Equation (18) cannot hold at a second north-south boundary at, say, $x = L$, at which the condition $M_L = 0$ must be satisfied. This inadequacy of our solution is due to the neglect of the field accelerations (eq. 4). Attempts will be made to find more general solutions and to study other special cases.

Substituting equation (18) in (9*b*):

$$\frac{\partial P}{\partial y} = -\Delta x \tan \varphi . \left(\frac{\overline{\partial \tau_x}}{\partial y} \tan \varphi + \frac{\overline{\partial^2 \tau_x}}{\partial y^2} R \right) + \tau_y \tag{19}$$

Equations (15) or (16) and (19), together with (14) and (18), represent in our special case the relationships of the distribution of mass and the corresponding mass transport to the wind stress. The validity of our results can be tested where suitable observations are available.

3. *Discussion.*—The available oceanographic observations comprise (1) a line of 8 stations between latitudes 22°N and 10°S, longitudes 137°W and 162°W, occupied by the *Carnegie* between October 21 and November 4, 1929 (Fleming[7]); (2) a line of 12 stations between latitudes 6°N and 9°S, longitudes 80°W and 108°W, occupied by the *Carnegie* between October 26 and November 21, 1928; and (3) a line of 8 stations between latitudes 9°N and 21°N, longitudes 87°W and 109°W, occupied by the Bushnell between March 18 and March 24, 1939 (Sverdrup[8]). From the observations at each of these stations the value of the function P was computed by integrating to a depth of 1000 meters. From all data the ratio $\Delta P/\Delta x$ was found, and from the *Carnegie* section in mid-ocean $\partial P/\partial y$ was derived.

Wind observations comprise (1) monthly wind roses for 5-degree squares published in the Pilot Charts of the North and South Pacific, giving the percentage of winds from different directions and the corresponding average wind force (on the Beaufort scale) and (2) compilations of frequencies of winds of different forces in the "Atlas of Climatological Charts of the Oceans."[9] From the wind data the average wind stresses in October and November were computed, using the relationship

$$\tau = \gamma^2 \rho' U^2$$

where γ^2 is the resistance coefficient, ρ' the density of the air, and U the wind speed as estimated at a height of about 10 meters. At wind force 3 Beaufort or less the sea surface was assumed to be hydrodynamically smooth, with a resistance coefficient of about 0.8×10^{-3}, decreasing somewhat with increasing wind speed. At wind force 4 Beaufort and higher a constant value, $\gamma^2 = 2.6 \times 10^{-3}$, was used, corresponding to a hydrodynamically rough surface (Rossby[10]). The manner in which all computations were carried out will be described elsewhere by the author and R. O. Reid, who has prepared the figures in this paper.

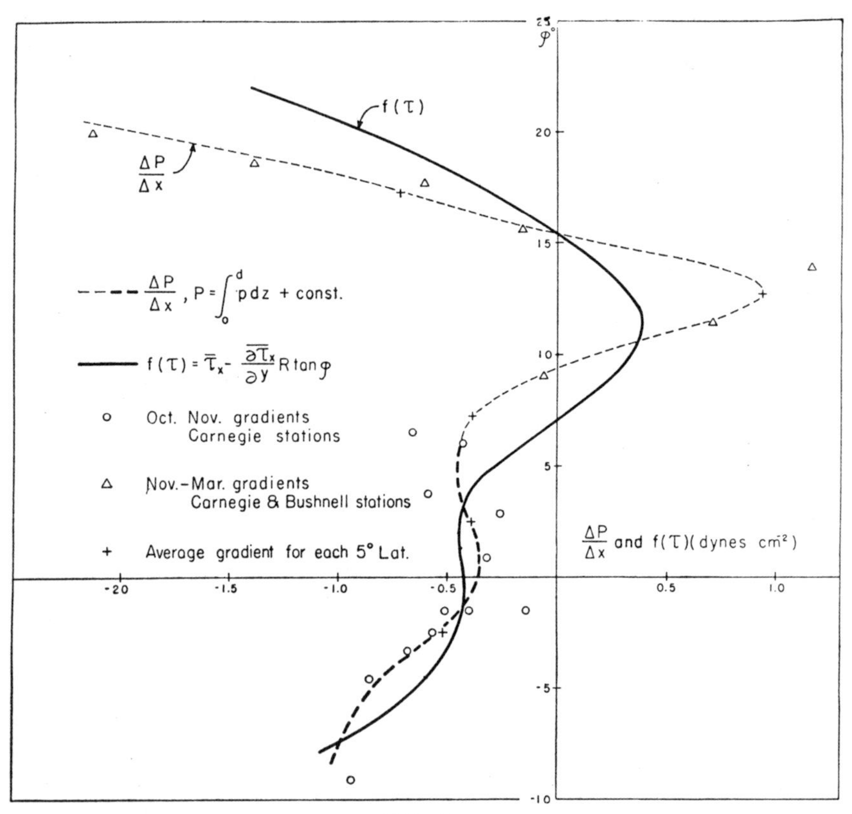

FIGURE 1

In figure 1 the terms of equation (16) are shown as functions of latitude. The curve that represents the left-hand term is heavily dashed to the south of latitude 6°N where the oceanographic observations upon which it is based were all taken in October–November, although in different years. To the north of 6°N the curve is shown by light dashes because observations off the American west coast in March have been combined with observations in mid-ocean in October. The right-hand term, the stress function, is shown by a full-drawn curve and is based on climatological wind data for the months October–November. The agreement between the curves is very good, considering that results of average wind conditions are compared with results derived from a few oceanographic stations which have been occupied in different seasons.

In figure 2 the P function and the terms of equation (19) are plotted against latitude. The P function is based on the *Carnegie* observations in mid-ocean in October–November, 1928, and the stress function on the average wind conditions in October–November over the ocean from the

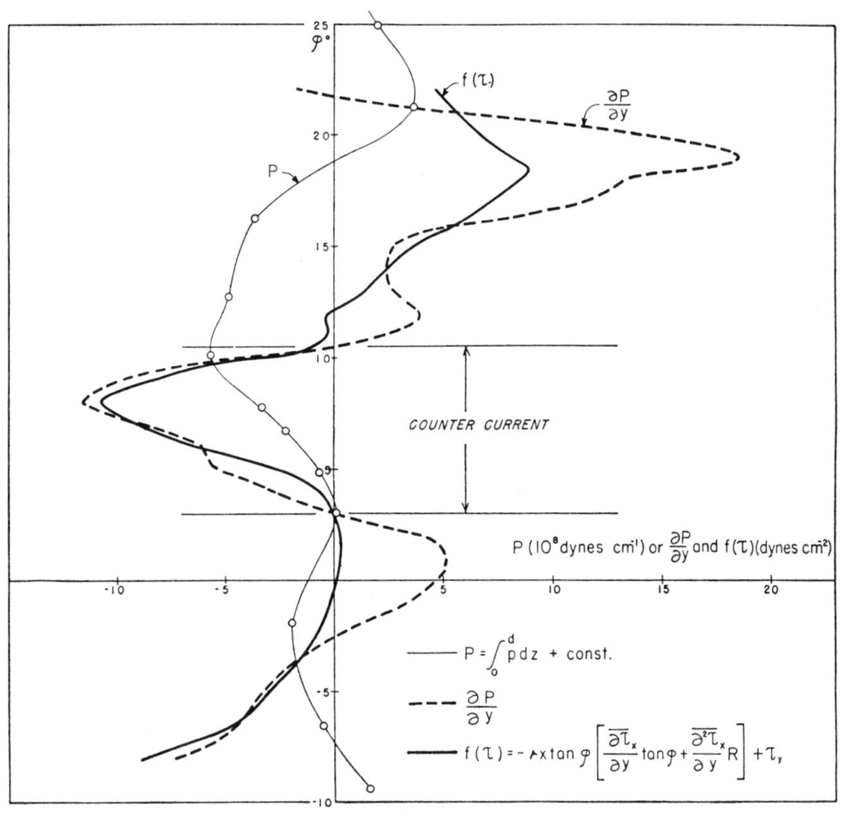

FIGURE 2

American west coast to the *Carnegie* section. A good agreement is obtained between the results based on a single oceanographic section and those derived from climatological wind charts.

4. Conclusions.—The distribution of density and the mass transport by the accompanying currents of the eastern equatorial Pacific depend entirely upon the average stress exerted on the sea surface by the prevailing winds. This conclusion is probably valid for the equatorial currents of all oceans but it has been demonstrated only for a case in which the non-linear terms in the equation of motion can be neglected.

It appears possible that the analysis of the relationship between wind stress and prevailing currents, assuming baroclinic conditions, can be extended to other cases and can be developed into a powerful tool for examining permanent currents as well as changes produced by changing winds. Efforts in this direction are being continued.

* Contributions from the Scripps Institution of Oceanography, New Series, No. 324.

[1] Ekman, V. W., *Annalen Hydrographie u. Mar. Met.*, **34,** 423–430 (1906).

[2] Stockmann, W., *Comptes rendus (Doklady) l'Acad. sci. l'U.R.S.S.*, **52,** 309–312 (1946).

[3] Fjeldstad, J. E., *Archiv Math. Naturvid.*, **48,** no. 6 (1946).

[4] Montgomery, R. B., and Palmén, E., *Jour. Marine Research*, **3,** 112–133 (1940).

[5] Ekman, V. W., *Gerlands Beitr. z. Geophysik*, **Suppl. 4** (1939).

[6] Defant, A., *Deutsche Atlantische Exped. "Meteor" 1925–27, Wiss. Ergebn.*, **4,** no. 2, 191–260 (1941).

[7] Fleming, J. A., *et al.*, *Sci. Results Cruise VII "Carnegie" 1928–29*, **I-B** (1945).

[8] Sverdrup, H. U., and Staff, *Records Observations, Scripps Institution of Oceanography*, **1,** 65–160 (1943).

[9] U. S. Weather Bureau, *W. B. No. 1247* (1938).

[10] Rossby, C.-G., *Papers Phys. Oceanography Meteorology*, **4,** no. 3 (1936).

The westward intensification of wind-driven ocean currents

H. Stommel

Reprinted with permission from Transactions, American Geophysical Union
Volume 29, Number 2,
pages 202 through 206, 1948

The Westward Intensification of Wind-Driven Ocean Currents

Henry Stommel
(*Contribution No. 408, Woods Hole Oceanographic Institution*)

ABSTRACT

A study is made of the wind-driven circulation in a homogeneous rectangular ocean under the influence of surface wind stress, linearised bottom friction, horizontal pressure gradients caused by a variable surface height, and Coriolis force.

An intense crowding of streamlines toward the western border of the ocean is discovered to be caused by variation of the Coriolis parameter with latitude. It is suggested that this process is the main reason for the formation of the intense currents (Gulf stream and others) observed in the actual oceans.

INTRODUCTION

Perhaps the most striking feature of the general oceanic wind-driven circulation is the intense crowding of streamlines near the western borders of the oceans. The Gulf Stream, the Kuroshio, and the Agulhas Current are examples of this phenomenon. The physical reason for the westward crowding of streamlines has always been obscure. The purpose of this paper is to study the dynamics of wind-driven oceanic circulation using analytically simple systems in an attempt to discover a physical parameter capable of producing the crowding of streamlines.

The phenomenon occurs along coastlines of such varied topography that it is clear that local topographic features do not significantly control the general streamline pattern. For the sake of simplicity the present study deals with flat rectangular oceans.

THE FORMULATION OF THE PROBLEM

A rectangular ocean is envisaged with the origin of a cartesian coordinate system at the southwest corner (see Fig. 1). The y axis points northward; the x axis eastward. The shores of the ocean are at $x = 0, \lambda$ and $y = 0, b$. The ocean is considered as a homogeneous layer of constant depth D when at rest. When currents occur, as in the real oceans, the depth differs from D everywhere by a small variable amount h. The quantity h is much smaller than D. The total depth of the water column is therefore $D + h$, D being everywhere constant, and h a variable yet to be determined.

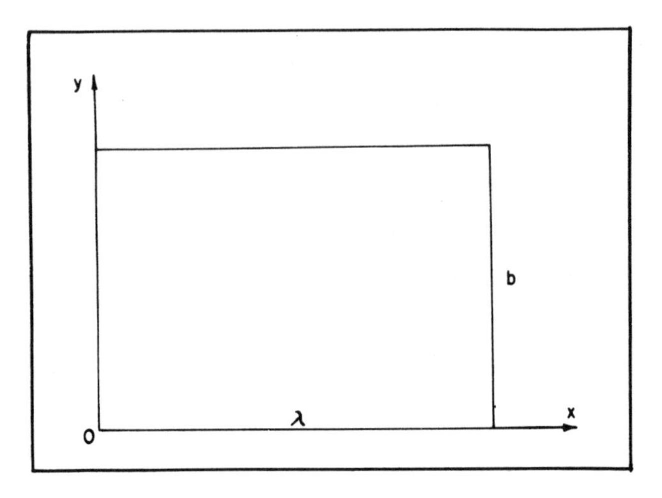

Fig. 1. Ocean basin dimensions and the coordinate system

The winds over the ocean are the Trades over the equatorial half of the rectangular basin, and Prevailing Westerlies over the poleward half. An expression for the wind stress acting upon a column of unit cross-section and depth $D + h$ must include this dependence upon y. A simple functional form of the wind stress is taken as $-F \cos(\pi y/b)$.

In order to keep the ocean from accelerating, a frictional dissipative term is required. To keep the equations of motion as simple as possible the component frictional forces are taken as $-Ru$ and $-Rv$, where R is the coefficient of friction, and u and v are the x and y components of the velocity vector, respectively. The Coriolis parameter f is also introduced. In general it is a function of y.

The steady state equations of motion, with the inertial terms omitted because they are small, are written in the form

$$0 = f(D + h)v - F \cos\left(\frac{\pi y}{b}\right) - Ru - g(D + h)\frac{\partial h}{\partial x} \tag{1}$$

$$0 = -f(D + h)u - Rv - g(D + h)\frac{\partial h}{\partial y}\,. \tag{2}$$

To these, the equation of continuity must be added

$$\frac{\partial}{\partial x}[(D+h)u] + \frac{\partial}{\partial y}[(D+h)v] = 0. \tag{3}$$

Cross-differentiation of (1) and (2) and use of (3) results in the following equation

$$v(D+h)\left(\frac{\partial f}{\partial y}\right) + \left(\frac{F\pi}{b}\right)\sin\left(\frac{\pi y}{b}\right) + R\left(\frac{\partial v}{\partial x} - \frac{\partial u}{\partial y}\right) = 0. \tag{4}$$

In the actual oceans h is so much smaller than D that to a first degree of approximation (4) may be rewritten as

$$\alpha v + \gamma \sin\left(\frac{\pi y}{b}\right) + \frac{\partial v}{\partial x} - \frac{\partial u}{\partial y} = 0 \tag{5}$$

where the following definitions have been made

$$\alpha = \left(\frac{D}{R}\right)\left(\frac{\partial f}{\partial y}\right) \qquad \gamma = \frac{F\pi}{Rb}. \tag{6}$$

To the same degree of approximation the equation of continuity (3) may be replaced by

$$\frac{\partial u}{\partial x} + \frac{\partial v}{\partial y} = 0. \tag{7}$$

A stream function ψ is introduced now by the following relations

$$u = \frac{\partial \psi}{\partial y} \qquad v = -\frac{\partial \psi}{\partial x}. \tag{8}$$

The equation (5) is now rewritten in terms of the stream function

$$\nabla^2\psi + \alpha\frac{\partial \psi}{\partial x} = \gamma \sin\left(\frac{\pi y}{b}\right). \tag{9}$$

The remainder of this paper is simply a study of solutions of this equation. The boundary conditions upon (9) are that the shore of the ocean be a streamline

$$\psi(0, y) = \psi(\lambda, y) = \psi(x, 0) = \psi(x, b) = 0. \tag{10}$$

FORMAL SOLUTION OF THE PROBLEM

If f is a linear function of y then α is a constant. Equation (9) is nonhomogeneous and therefore cannot be solved directly by separation of variables. If the right hand member is dropped, the resulting homogeneous equation is soluble by separation. Adding the solution of the homogeneous equation to a particular integral of (9) gives the general solution of (9). A particular integral of (9) is, by inspection

$$-\gamma\left(\frac{b}{\pi}\right)^2 \sin\left(\frac{\pi y}{b}\right). \tag{11}$$

The homogeneous equation is

$$\nabla^2\psi + \alpha\frac{\partial\psi}{\partial x} = 0. \tag{12}$$

To solve (9) by separation of variables let ψ be given in the following form

$$\psi = XY; \tag{13}$$

X is a function of x only, and Y is a function of y only. Equation (9) may therefore be written as the following system

$$Y'' + n^2 Y = 0 \tag{14}$$

$$X'' + \alpha X' - n^2 X = 0. \tag{15}$$

The primes represent total differentiation, and n^2 is determined by the conditions (10). The general solutions of these two equations are in series form

$$Y = \Sigma(c_j \sin n_j y + d_j \cos n_j y) \tag{16}$$

$$X = \Sigma(p_j e^{A_j x} + q_j e^{B_j x}). \tag{17}$$

The constants A_j and B_j have been defined thus

$$A_j = -\alpha/2 + \sqrt{\alpha^2/4 + n_j^2}, \text{ and } B_j = -\alpha/2 - \sqrt{\alpha^2/4 + n_j^2}.$$

The quantities c_j, d_j, p_j, q_j, are undetermined constants. The general solution of (9) is therefore

$$\psi = XY - \gamma\left(\frac{b}{\pi}\right)^2 \sin\left(\frac{\pi y}{b}\right). \tag{18}$$

This solution is very general but reduces to a simple closed form when the boundary conditions (10) are imposed. First of all, the d_j and c_j vanish except c_1 corresponding to $n_1 = \pi/b$. This constant c_1 may be absorbed into p_1 and q_1. Dropping subscripts the stream function now has the form

$$\psi = \gamma\left(\frac{b}{\pi}\right)^2 \sin\left(\frac{\pi y}{b}\right)[pe^{Ax} + qe^{Bx} - 1] \tag{19}$$

where

$$p = (1 - e^{B\lambda})/(e^{A\lambda} - e^{B\lambda}) \text{ and } q = 1 - p. \tag{20}$$

The curves (ψ = const.) are the streamlines of the ocean currents.

The velocity components u and v may be obtained from (8) by simple differentiation of the stream function

$$u = \gamma \left(\frac{b}{\pi}\right)^2 \cos\left(\frac{\pi y}{b}\right)(pe^{Ax} + qe^{Bx} - 1) \tag{21}$$

$$v = -\gamma \left(\frac{b}{\pi}\right)^2 \sin\left(\frac{\pi y}{b}\right)(pAe^{Ax} + qBe^{Bx}). \tag{22}$$

The value of h at any point referred to the value of h at the origin may now be obtained by integration of (1) and (2).

$$\begin{aligned} h(x, y) = &-\left(\frac{F}{gD}\right)\left(e^{Ax}\frac{p}{A} + e^{Bx}\frac{q}{B}\right) - \left(\frac{b}{\pi}\right)^2\left(\frac{F}{gD}\right)(pAe^{Ax} \\ &+ qBe^{Bx})\left[\left(\cos\frac{\pi y}{b}\right) - 1\right] - \left\{\left(\frac{f\gamma}{g}\right)\left(\frac{b}{\pi}\right)^2 \sin\left(\frac{\pi y}{b}\right)\right. \\ &\left. - \left(\frac{\partial f}{\partial y}\right)\left(\frac{\gamma}{g}\right)\left(\frac{b}{\pi}\right)^3\left[\cos\left(\frac{\pi y}{b}\right) - 1\right]\right\}(pe^{Ax} + qe^{Bx} - 1). \end{aligned} \tag{23}$$

DISCUSSION OF THE SOLUTION FOR CERTAIN OCEAN SYSTEMS

In order to clarify the meaning of the foregoing section, it is advisable to see what role the various parameters play by working some numerical examples. Three cases are discussed. All involve the same effects of wind stress, bottom friction, and horizontal pressure gradients caused by variations of surface height. The role of the Coriolis force is different in each case. First it is assumed that the Coriolis parameter vanishes everywhere, the case of the non-rotating ocean. Secondly, it is assumed that the Coriolis parameter is constant everywhere, the case of the uniformly rotating ocean. In the third case it is assumed that the Coriolis parameter is a linear function of latitude. Of the three cases, the last one most nearly approximates the state of affairs in the real ocean.

For convenience of the numerical computations the dimensions of the ocean are taken as follows

$$\lambda = 10^9 \text{ cm} = 10{,}000 \text{ km}$$

$$b = 2\pi \times 10^8 \text{ cm} = 6249 \text{ km}$$

$$D = 2 \times 10^4 \text{ cm} = 200 \text{ m}.$$

The maximum wind stress F is taken to be one dyne/cm^2.

The coefficient of friction R is the only quantity for which a value must be devised. If a value of $R = 0.02$ is assumed, the velocities in the resulting systems approach those observed in nature.

THE CASE OF THE NON-ROTATING OCEAN

In this case the constants p and q are particularly simple. Within one per cent, or as closely as graphs may be drawn, p and q are given by

$$p = e^{-\pi\lambda/b} \qquad q = 1.$$

The equation for the stream function is therefore

$$\psi = \gamma(b/\pi)^2 \sin(\pi y/b)[e^{(x-\lambda)\pi/b} + e^{-x\pi/b} - 1].$$

The east-west and north-south symmetry of the streamlines is immediately evident from this equation, and the actual streamlines computed from it are exhibited in Figure 2.

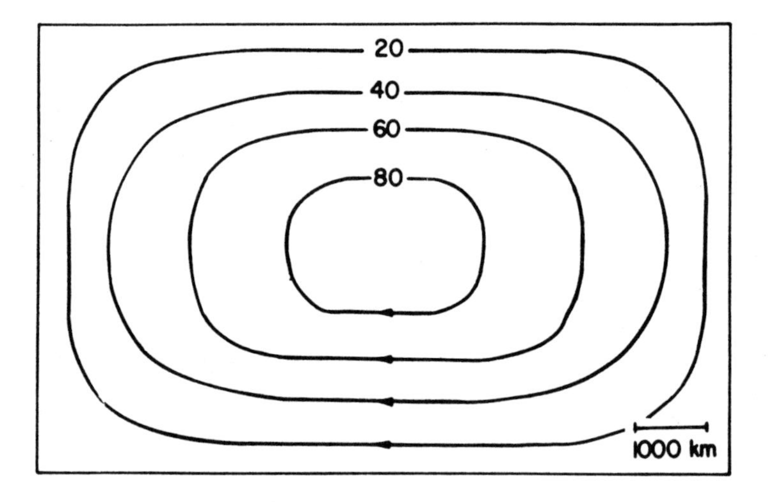

Fig. 2. Streamlines for the case of both the non-rotating and uniformly rotating oceans

The height contours are computed from (23). Since in this case there is no Coriolis force, the last two terms vanish. Height contours according to this equation are plotted in Figure 3. The general features of the non-rotating wind-driven system are a broad circulation exhibiting absolutely no tendency toward crowding of the streamlines.

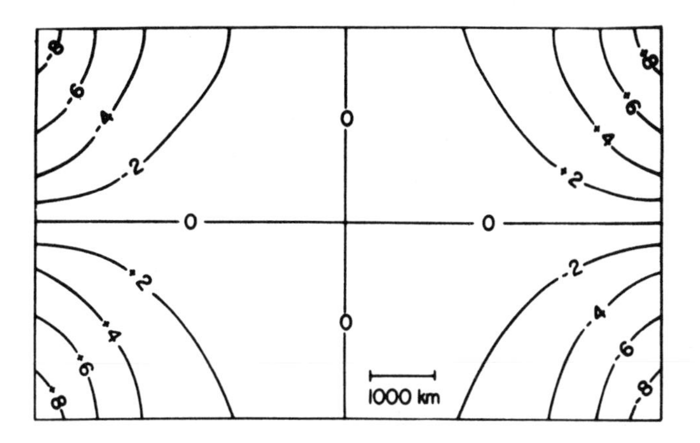

Fig. 3. Surface height contours for the non-rotating ocean in cm

THE CASE OF THE UNIFORMLY ROTATING OCEAN

In the case where the Coriolis parameter is a constant 0.25×10^{-4}, the streamline diagram does not differ from that of the non-rotating basin. When the height contours are computed however from (23), a difference between the two cases becomes apparent. The third term which vanished in the first case does not vanish in this case. Height contours computed from this equation are exhibited in Figure 4. The large elevation in the central portion of the ocean provides horizontal pressure gradients that largely counterbalance the Coriolis forces. The height contours are not strictly parallel to the streamlines but nearly so.

THE CASE WHERE THE CORIOLIS PARAMETER IS A LINEAR FUNCTION OF LATITUDE

In the real ocean the Coriolis force is a function of latitude. In low latitudes this function is nearly a linear one $f = y \times 10^{-13}$. The inequality in the absolute values of the quantities A and B that occurs in this case immediately makes clear the complete lack of

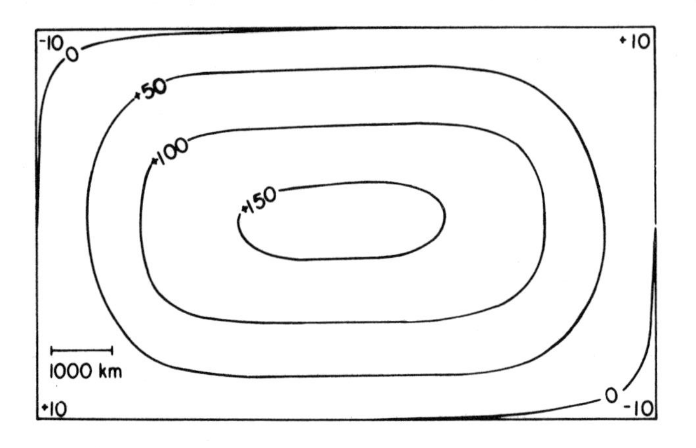

Fig. 4. Surface height contours for the uniformly rotating ocean in cm referred to an arbitrary level

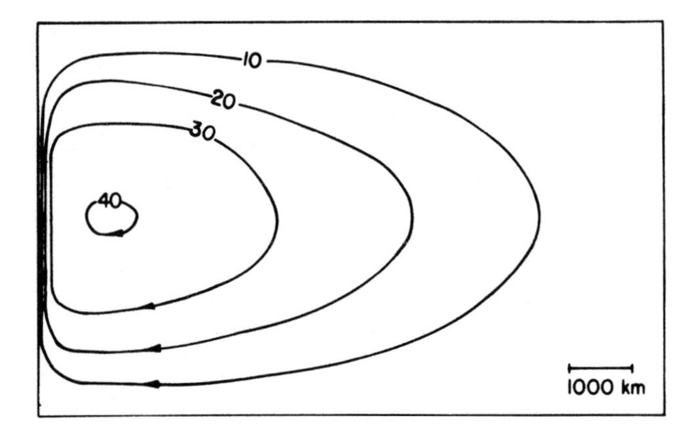

Fig. 5. Streamlines for the case where the Coriolis force is a linear function of latitude

east-west symmetry. The streamlines drawn from this formula are shown in Figure 5. The most striking feature of this figure is the intense crowding of streamlines toward the western border of the ocean. The rest of the streamline picture is broad and diffuse. The velocity of this system in the region corresponding to the location of the equatorial current (in the actual oceans) is about 20 cm/sec.

At the western border the northward velocity amounts to as much as 240 cm/sec. The width of the region of strong northward currents is less than 100 km. The similarity that the velocity field of this simple case bears to that of the actual Gulf Stream suggests that the westward concentration of streamlines in the wind-driven oceanic circulation is a result of the variation of the Coriolis parameter with latitude.

The height contours computed from this case are shown in Figure 6. To extend the results of this study to the Southern Hemisphere the reader will notice that since α is unaffected by crossing the Equator and γ simply changes sign, all the diagrams may be transformed to below the Equator by simple reflection across the x axis. The crowding of streamlines is therefore toward the western border of each ocean, irrespective of hemisphere.

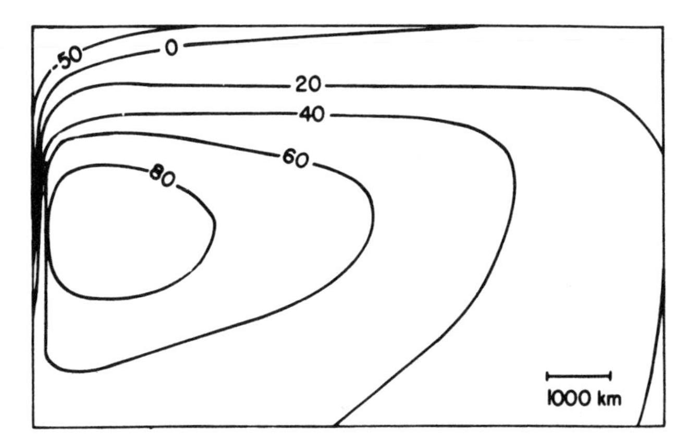

Fig. 6. Surface height contours in cm for the case where the Coriolis parameter is a linear function of latitude

The artificial nature of this theoretical model should be emphasized, particularly the form of dissipative term. The writer thinks of this work as suggestive, certainly not conclusive. The many features of actual ocean structure omitted in the model should be evident.

Woods Hole Oceanographic Institution,
Woods Hole, Massachusetts

(*Manuscript received September 25, 1947; presented at the New England Meeting, Woods Hole, Massachusetts, September 18, 1947; open for formal discussion until September 1, 1948.*)

On the wind-driven ocean circulation

W. H. Munk

Reprinted with permission from
Journal of Meterology
Volume 7, Number 2,
pages 79 through 93, 1950

On the Wind-Driven Ocean Circulation

By Walter H. Munk

Institute of Geophysics and Scripps Institution of Oceanography University of California[1]

(*Manuscript received 24 September 1949*)

ABSTRACT

Streamlines of oceanic mass transport are derived from solutions to a vertically integrated vorticity equation which relates planetary vorticity, lateral stress curl, and the curl of the stress exerted by the winds on the sea surface. These solutions account for many of the gross features of the general ocean circulation, and some of its details, on the basis of the observed mean annual winds.

The solution for *zonal winds* (section 3) gives the main gyres of the ocean circulation. The northern and southern boundaries of these gyres are the west wind drift, the equatorial currents, and equatorial counter-current. They are determined by the westerly winds, the trades, and the doldrums, respectively. For each gyre the solution gives the following observed features (from west to east): a concentrated current (*e.g.*, the Gulf Stream), a countercurrent, boundary vortices (the Sargasso Sea), and a steady compensating drift. Using mean Atlantic zonal winds, the solution yields a transport for the Gulf Stream of 36 million metric tons per second, compared to 74 million as derived from oceanographic observations. The discrepancy can probably be ascribed, at least in part, to an underestimate of the wind stress at low wind speeds (Beaufort 4 and less) as derived from the relationship now generally accepted.

The solution for *meridional winds* (section 5) accounts for the main features of the current system off California. For a *circular wind system* (section 8) the solution gives a *wind-spun* vortex which is displaced westward in relation to the wind system, in agreement with observations in the Northeast Pacific high-pressure area.

Based on these three solutions, a general nomenclature of ocean currents is introduced (section 9), applicable to all oceans regardless of hemisphere, and suggestive of the meteorologic features to which the currents are so closely related. In the light of this general system, the circulations of the northern and southern hemispheres, and of the North Atlantic and North Pacific are compared (section 10). Rossby's jet-stream theory of the Gulf Stream, and Maury's theory of thermo-

[1] Contribution from the Scripps Institution of Oceanography, New Series, No. 462. This paper was prepared partly under a Guggenheim Fellowship at the University of Oslo, partly with the support of the Office of Naval Research.

haline circulation are discussed, and it is concluded that the circulation in the upper layers of the oceans are the result chiefly of the stresses exerted by the winds.

1. INTRODUCTION

This study is a resumption of Ekman's (1923; 1932) intensive effort to account theoretically for the main features in the general ocean circulation. The temptation to reopen this problem is provided by three recent developments: (*a*) Rossby's (1936) introduction of lateral stresses associated with the horizontal exchange of large eddies; (*b*) Sverdrup's (1947) computation of the equatorial countercurrents in a baroclinic ocean from the known wind stress; and (*c*) Stommel's (1948) explanation of the westward intensification of a wind-induced circulation in terms of the variation of the Coriolis parameter with latitude.

In Ekman's and Stommel's model the ocean is assumed homogeneous, a case in which the currents extend to the very bottom. Not only is this in contrast with observations, according to which the bulk of the water transport in the main ocean currents takes place in the upper thousand meters, but it also leads to mathematical complications which rendered Ekman's analysis very difficult, and forced Stommel to resort to a rather arbitrary frictional force along the bottom.

To avoid these difficulties, we retain Sverdrup's integrated mass transport as the dependent variable. This device makes it possible to examine the more general case of a baroclinic ocean without having to specify the nature of the vertical distributions of density and current. In recognition of the evidence that currents essentially vanish at great depths, we shall depend on lateral friction for the dissipative forces. From Stommel we retain the rectangular boundaries, although we extend the basin to both sides of the equator and deal with the *observed* wind distribution rather than simple sinusoidal distribution.

2. THE DIFFERENTIAL EQUATION OF MASS TRANSPORT

Let the x-axis point eastward along the equator, the y-axis northward, and the z-axis vertically upwards from a level surface (assumed plane) just beneath the sea surface (unit vectors $\mathbf{i}$, $\mathbf{j}$, $\mathbf{k}$). For the present, the nonlinear inertial terms are considered negligible, an assumption which will be examined in section 10. The equations of steady horizontal motion for a unit volume are

$$\nabla_H p + f\mathbf{k} \times (\rho \mathbf{v}_H) - \frac{\partial}{\partial x}\left(A'_H \frac{\partial \mathbf{v}_H}{\partial x}\right) - \frac{\partial}{\partial y}\left(A'_H \frac{\partial \mathbf{v}_H}{\partial y}\right) - \frac{\partial}{\partial z}\left(A'_V \frac{\partial \mathbf{v}_H}{\partial z}\right) = 0, \quad (1)$$

where $\nabla_H = \mathbf{i}\ \partial/\partial x + \mathbf{j}\ \partial/\partial y$, p is pressure, ρ is density, $\mathbf{v}_H = \mathbf{i}v_x + \mathbf{j}v_y$ is the two-dimensional (horizontal) velocity vector, and $f = 2\omega \sin \varphi$ is twice the vertical component at latitude φ of the earth's angular velocity ω. Observations have shown that A'_V, the dynamic eddy viscosity associated with vertical shear, is different from A'_H, the eddy viscosity pertaining to horizontal shear, the two coefficients bearing a ratio rather larger than that of the width of the ocean currents to their depth. We shall assume A'_H horizontally isotropic, neglecting variations that might be related to differences between zonal and meridional motions of large horizontal eddies on a rotating earth.

The equations of motion will be integrated from some constant depth, $-h$, beneath which the motion and horizontal pressure gradients essentially vanish (Sverdrup, 1947), to the surface, $z = z_0(x, y)$. Let

$$P = \int_{-h}^{z_0} p\ dz, \qquad \mathbf{M}_H = \int_{-h}^{z_0} \rho\ \mathbf{v}_H\ dz, \qquad (2a, b)$$

designate the integrated pressure and mass transport. Then

$$\int_{-h}^{z_0} \nabla_H p\ dz = \nabla_H P - p_{z_0} \nabla_H z_0,$$

where p_{z_0} is the atmospheric pressure and $\nabla_H z_0$ is the gradient of the sea surface. The second term is negligible for the present investigation.

The integration of the horizontal shearing forces is more cumbersome. The simplest form is $A_H \nabla^2_H \mathbf{M}$, where A_H is an effective kinematic eddy viscosity which is assumed independent of x and y. There is no evidence to indicate that the complicated expression given by a complete integral with a variable $A_H = A'_H/\rho$ would be a more accurate description of the forces. Finally

$$\int_{-h}^{z_0} \frac{\partial}{\partial z}\left(A'_V \frac{\partial \mathbf{v}_H}{\partial z}\right) dz = \left[A'_V \frac{\partial \mathbf{v}_H}{\partial z}\right]_{z_0} - \left[A'_V \frac{\partial \mathbf{v}_H}{\partial z}\right]_{-h} = \boldsymbol{\tau}, \quad (3)$$

where $\boldsymbol{\tau}$ is the stress applied by the wind on the sea surface. In most ocean areas it is adequate to select a depth h of 1000–2000 meters, which is comfortably above the sea bottom. The foregoing equation could be used even where the current extends to the bottom, provided $\boldsymbol{\tau}$ would then designate surface stress minus bottom stress.

With the understanding that all operators and vectors have only horizontal components, the subscript H can be dropped, and the integrated equations of motion become

$$\nabla P + f\mathbf{k} \times \mathbf{M} - \boldsymbol{\tau} - A\nabla^2\mathbf{M} = 0. \tag{4}$$

The vertical integration enables us, therefore, to avoid any assumptions regarding the variation of A'_V with depth, and to postpone an examination of the density and velocity structure in depth.

The surface kinematic boundary condition requires w_{z_0} to vanish for steady state; furthermore it has been assumed that $w_{-h} = 0$. Therefore $\nabla \cdot \mathbf{M} = 0$, or $M_x = -\partial\psi/\partial y$, $M_y = \partial\psi/\partial x$, *i.e.*,

$$\mathbf{M} = \mathbf{k} \times \nabla\psi, \tag{5}$$

where ψ is the mass-transport stream function (dimensions: mass/time). Substituting ψ into (4) and performing the curl operation to eliminate P gives the differential equation of mass transport

$$\boxed{(A\nabla^4 - \beta\, \partial/\partial x)\psi = -\mathrm{curl}_z\, \boldsymbol{\tau},} \tag{6}$$

where $\mathrm{curl}_z\, \boldsymbol{\tau}$ is the vertical component of the windstress curl, $\nabla^4 = \partial^4/\partial x^4 + 2\, \partial^4/\partial x^2\partial y^2 + \partial^4/\partial y^4$ is the biharmonic operator, and $\beta = df/dy$ is the rate of change northward of twice the vertical component of the earth's angular velocity.

Equation (6) is an integrated version of the vorticity equation. Ekman calls $\beta\, \partial\psi/\partial x = \beta M_y$ the planetary vorticity. Accordingly, the vorticity equation (6) expresses a balance between lateral stress curl, planetary vorticity and wind-stress curl.

For boundary conditions we choose

$$\psi_{\mathrm{bdry}} = 0, \qquad (\partial\psi/\partial\nu)_{\mathrm{bdry}} = 0, \tag{7a, b}$$

where ν is normal to the boundary. The first equation states that the boundary itself is a streamline (whose value is arbitrarily selected as zero); the second equation states that no slippage takes place against the boundary.

The problem is to solve (6) subject to boundary conditions (7). Hidaka (1949) has given the formal solution employing the transformation into a variational problem. There is a remarkable analogy between this problem and a problem arising in the theory of elasticity (Rayleigh, 1893; Love, 1944, p. 464). The deflection ψ of a plate of uniform flexural rigidity A, clamped at its boundaries and subjected to a load $-\text{curl}_z\, \boldsymbol{\tau}$ is governed by

$$A\nabla^4\psi = -\text{curl}_z\, \boldsymbol{\tau}, \tag{8}$$

subject to boundary conditions (7). Equation (6) reduces to this form when the planetary vorticity is negligible, a condition that might arise in high latitudes ($\beta \approx 0$) and for quasizonal flow ($M_y \approx 0$). The analogy suggests experimental methods for finding streamlines under complex wind stress and boundary conditions.

3. SOLUTION FOR ZONAL WINDS

A rectangular ocean is assumed, extending from $x = 0$ to $x = r$, and from $y = -s$ to $y = +s$. One may think that such an arbitrary choice of ocean boundaries would make it impossible to deal with actual conditions. Yet the proper solution for the *main features* in the ocean circulation can be expected to be rather insensitive to the choice of boundaries, because these main features are similar in all oceans (table 3) although the boundaries are not. The boundary conditions (7) become

$$\psi = 0, \qquad \partial\psi/\partial x = 0, \qquad \text{for } x = 0, \quad x = r; \tag{9}$$

$$\psi = 0, \qquad \partial\psi/\partial y = 0, \qquad \text{for } y = -s, y = s. \tag{10}$$

For a *zonal* wind circulation ($\tau_y = 0$) the stress on the sea surface in the interval $-s < y < +s$ can be written as a sum of terms like

$$\tau_{xn} = a \cos ny + b \sin ny + c$$

where $n = j\pi/s$, $j = 1, 2, \cdots$ *etc.* The vertical component of the wind-stress curl is then a sum of terms like

$$\text{curl}_{zn}\, \boldsymbol{\tau} = -\partial\tau_{xn}/\partial y = n(a \sin ny - b \cos ny), \tag{11}$$

and the particular integral of (6) becomes

$$\psi_{pn} = -n^{-3}A^{-1}(a \sin ny - b \cos ny) = -n^{-4}A^{-1}\, \text{curl}_{zn}\, \tau. \tag{12}$$

Let $k = \sqrt[3]{\beta/A}$ designate the *Coriolis-friction* wave number, assumed constant. The solution to the homogeneous equation

$$(\nabla^4 - k^3\, \partial/\partial x)\psi_{hn} = 0 \tag{13}$$

can be written as a product of $(a \sin ny - b \cos ny)$ and a function of x. For later convenience we choose the form

$$\psi_{hn} = \psi_{pn}(rAn^4\beta^{-1}X_n - 1), \tag{14}$$

where X is a function of x to be determined below. The complete integral equals

$$\psi_n = \psi_{pn} + \psi_{hn} = rAn^4X_n\beta^{-1}\psi_{pn},$$

or

$$\psi_n = -rX_n\beta^{-1} \operatorname{curl}_{zn} \boldsymbol{\tau}. \tag{15}$$

It follows from (12), (13) and (14) that the function $X_n(x)$ must obey the differential equation

$$X'''' - 2n^2X'' - k^3X' + n^4X = \beta/rA = k^3/r,$$

which yields
$$(\gamma_n{}^4kr)X = 1 + \tfrac{1}{2}(p_1 + ip_2)e^{\alpha_1 kx} + \tfrac{1}{2}(p_1 - ip_2)e^{\alpha_2 kx} + pe_3{}^{\alpha_3 kx} + p_4e^{\alpha_4 kx},$$
where $\gamma = n/k$ is the essential nondimensional number in this investigation, and where α_1, α_2, α_3, α_4 are the roots of the characteristic equation

$$(\alpha^2 - \gamma_n{}^2)^2 = \alpha. \tag{16}$$

This equation has two complex roots, $\alpha_1' + i\alpha_1''$, $\alpha_2' + i\alpha_2''$, and two real roots, α_3', α_4' (fig. 1). For small values of γ,

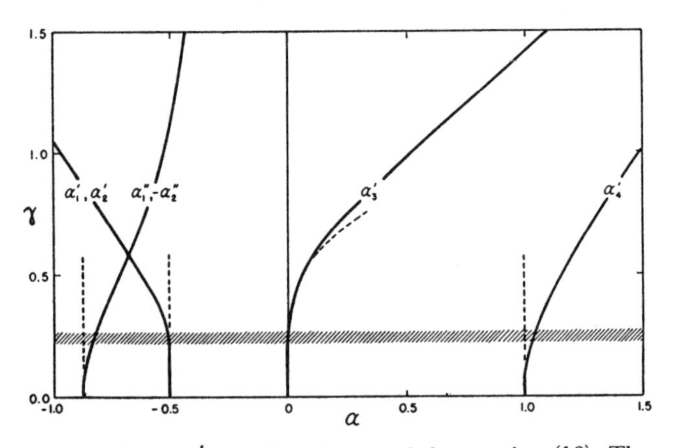

Fig. 1. Roots $\alpha' + i\alpha''$ to characteristic equation (16). The dashed lines give the asymptotic solutions for $\gamma \ll 1$ which have been applied to the large scale features ($\gamma < 0.25$) in the ocean circulation.

$$\alpha_1 = -\tfrac{1}{2}(1 + i\sqrt{3}), \qquad \alpha_3 = \gamma_n{}^4, \tag{17}$$
$$\alpha_2 = -\tfrac{1}{2}(1 - i\sqrt{3}), \qquad \alpha_4 = 1,$$

as shown by the dotted lines in fig. 1. The boundary conditions (9) give

$$-p_1 \approx -p_2\sqrt{3} \approx 1 + p_3 \approx p_4 \approx \gamma_n{}^4 kr, \tag{18}$$

provided

$$\gamma_n{}^4 \ll 1, \qquad e^{-kr} \ll 1, \qquad e^{-\gamma_n{}^4 kr} \approx 1 - \gamma_n{}^4 kr. \tag{19}$$

Subject to these approximations,

$$X = -Ke^{-\frac{1}{2}kx} \cos\left(\frac{\sqrt{3}}{2}\, kx + \frac{\sqrt{3}}{2kr} - \frac{\pi}{6}\right) + 1 - \frac{1}{kr}\,[kx - e^{-k(r-x)} - 1] \tag{20}$$

$$\frac{X'}{k} = Ke^{-\frac{1}{2}kx} \sin\left(\frac{\sqrt{3}}{2}\, kx + \frac{\sqrt{3}}{2kr}\right) - \frac{1}{kr}\,[1 - e^{-k(r-x)}], \tag{21}$$

central

east

west

where $K = 2/\sqrt{3} - \sqrt{3}/kr$. The meaning of the horizontal braces will be discussed later.

The important thing to notice is that, to the present degree of approximation, X does not depend on n; *i.e.*, that the response of the current to the zonal wind stress is without distortion in the y-direction for $\gamma \ll 1$. Equation (15) can therefore be written

$$\boxed{\psi = -rX\beta^{-1} \operatorname{curl}_z \boldsymbol{\tau},} \tag{22}$$

and the stream function computed directly from the observed (zonal) stress without expanding the stress in a Fourier series, provided such a series converges so rapidly that for all significant terms conditions (19) are fulfilled. Whether this is the case can usually be told by inspection. Anticipating the numerical values $k = .016\ \text{km}^{-1}$, $r = 6000$ km, conditions (19) for 10 per cent accuracy in ψ give $\gamma < 0.25$, corresponding to a minimum zonal wave length $2\pi/n$ of about 1500

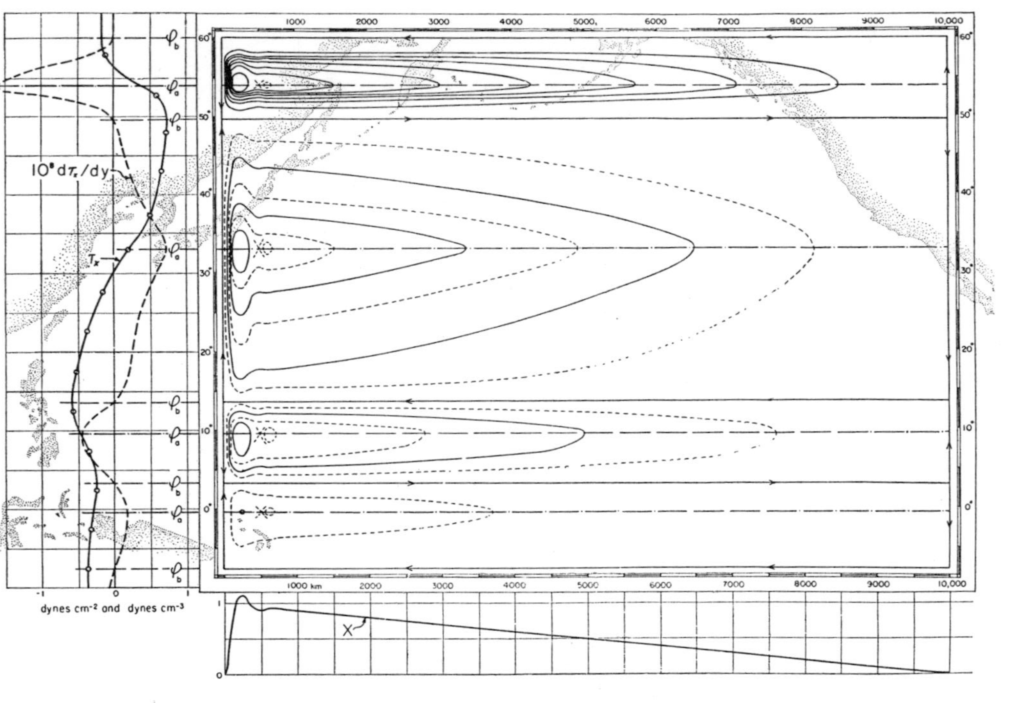

Fig. 2. The mean annual zonal wind stress $\tau_x(y)$ over the Pacific and its curl $d\tau_x/dy$ are plotted on the left, the function $X(x)$ on the lower part. These functions have been combined graphically according to equation (22) to give mass transport streamlines $\psi(x,y)$. The transport between adjacent solid lines is 10×10^{12} g sec^{-1}, or 10 million metric tons sec^{-1}. The total transport between the coast and any point x, y is $\psi(x,y)$. The chart of the Pacific has a uniform distance scale throughout. In the relatively narrow northern portion, the transport is greatly exaggerated.

km. For the mean annual stress distribution (fig. 2) the shortest wave length of the important N-S variations is the distance between the northern and southern trades, 4000 km. *The approximations leading up to (22) appear to be valid for a study of the general ocean circulation as it is related to the general atmospheric circulation.*

For stationary compact cyclones and sharp fronts with *overtones* of less than 1500 km wave length ($\gamma > 0.25$), it is necessary to compute separately the components ψ_n for each component wind stress τ_n according to equation (15), and to sum. The roots α can be read off fig. 1 and the p's determined by the original boundary conditions (9).

There remain the conditions (10) at the northern and southern boundaries. We note (fig. 9) that the winds are weak at 60°–70° latitudes, and we shall satisfy (10) by assuming $\text{curl}_z\, \tau$ and its derivative to approach zero at these boundaries. It must be admitted that this easy way of satisfying boundary conditions is aided by the present lack of adequate wind data in high latitudes.

To the extent to which these conditions on $\text{curl}_z\, \tau$ are not satisfied there must be deviations from the present solution, but we may expect these deviations to be restricted to relatively narrow zones adjacent to the northern and southern boundaries for the following reasons: The general circulations in the Atlantic and Pacific Oceans are in a very rough sense symmetrical with respect to the equator (except for an asymmetry related to the asymmetry of the wind circulation), whereas the boundaries are not. To the south all oceans open into the Antarctic Sea, to the north they are practically closed. Even the Indian Ocean, with its northern boundary only 1000–2000 km north of the equator, has about the same circulation in its central and southern parts as the Atlantic and Pacific.

It is none the less possible that important features have escaped us by the present incomplete treatment, and we hope to be able to give a complete numerical solution (for actual boundaries) at a later time. The similar but much simpler problem of a rectangular plate clamped at its edges and subject to a uniform load (equations 8, 9, 10 with $\text{curl}_z\, \tau$ constant) has received considerable attention, yet no complete theoretical solution has been found, and recourse has had to be made to rather elaborate numerical methods (Love, 1944, pp. 493–497). We note, however, that the solution in the vicinity of the transverse axis (corresponding to low and middle latitudes) for a plate which is more than twice as long as broad is practically the same as if the length were infinite.

4. ZONAL WIND CURRENTS

The wind stress has been computed for the North Pacific and the North and Central Atlantic for each month and 5-degree quadrangle. The source material consisted of the wind roses on the U. S. Hydrographic Office Pilot Charts of the North Pacific Ocean, the summary of Marine Data Cards of the U. S. Weather Bureau, and the Monthly Meteorological Charts of the Atlantic Ocean prepared by the Meteorological Office, Air Ministry, London. The variability of the wind and the hydrodynamic character of the sea surface has been taken into account in the manner described by Reid (1948). Fig. 2 shows the mass transport streamlines $\psi(x, y)$ in a rectangular ocean computed from (22) for the mean annual *zonal* winds over the Pacific. The topography of the free surface and of other isobaric surfaces is related to the ψ-topography, the relationship depending however on the vertical density structure. For the equatorial Pacific, Reid (1948b) has successfully used a simple model of vertical density distribution consisting of a homogeneous layer of density ρ_0 and thickness h' above an *exponential* layer of density $\rho_{-\infty} - (\rho_{-\infty} - \rho_0) \exp(1 + z/h')$. He finds

$$P + constant = \tfrac{5}{8}g \frac{\rho_0{}^2}{\rho_{-\infty} - \rho_0} z_0{}^2 = (5/2)g(\rho_{-\infty} - \rho_0)h'^2 \approx f\psi \qquad (23)$$

for the elevation z_0 of the surface above, and the depression of h' beneath their mean level.

The major ocean gyres.—The zonal wind system divides the ocean circulation into a number of gyres, each bounded by latitudes φ_b for which $M_y = 0$, or by (22),

$$\text{curl}_z\, \boldsymbol{\tau} = 0 \text{ at } \varphi = \varphi_b.$$

The major dividing lines between gyres correspond to the latitudes of maximum west winds, of the northerly and southerly trades, and of the doldrums (fig. 2). These compare favorably with those determined from oceanographic observations.

The latitudinal *axis* of each gyre may be defined by $M_x = 0$, or

$$\frac{d}{dy}\frac{\text{curl}_z\, \boldsymbol{\tau}}{\beta} = 0 \approx \frac{d^2\tau_x}{dy^2} \qquad \text{at} \qquad \varphi = \varphi_a.$$

The Atlantic Sargasso Sea is associated with the inflection point in the mean wind stress curve between the westerly winds and the north-easterly trades.[2] The inflection points between the doldrums and the northern and southern trades determine the boundaries of the equatorial countercurrent.

The western currents.—Along any fixed latitude, ψ varies with X only, and the curves $X(x)$ and $X'(x)$ in fig. 3 can be interpreted as the north–south component of transport, and transport per unit length, drawn to an arbitrary scale. For definiteness, consider sections at latitudes φ_a through the center of gyres.

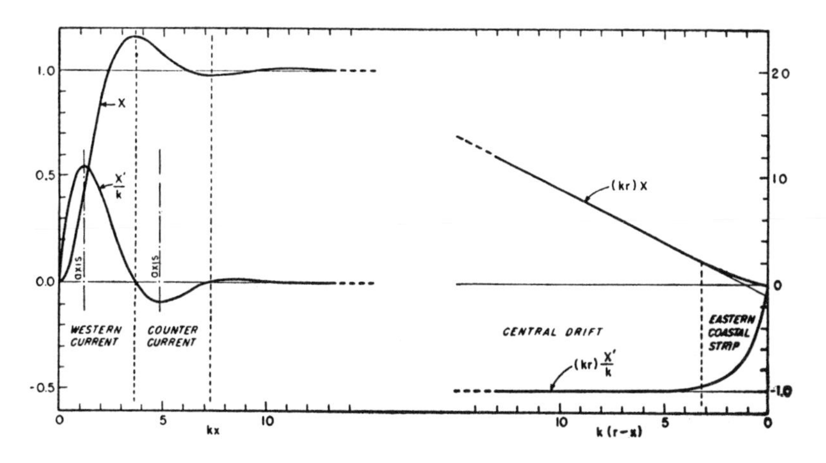

Fig. 3. Plot of equations (20) and (21), giving the west–east variation in transport ($\sim X$) and transport velocity ($\sim X'$) from the western shore ($x = 0$) to the eastern shore ($r - x = 0$). The scale for the central and eastern solutions is exaggerated relative to the scale for the western solution.

When X and X' are computed from (20) and (21), it is found that the equations fall naturally into three parts, each of which dominates in a given sector. At the western edge of the ocean $x \ll r$, and

$$X_W = -\frac{2}{\sqrt{3}} e^{-\frac{1}{2}kx} \cos\left(\frac{\sqrt{3}}{2} kx - \frac{\pi}{6}\right) + 1, \tag{20W}$$

$$\frac{X'_W}{k} = \frac{2}{\sqrt{3}} e^{-\frac{1}{2}kx} \sin \frac{\sqrt{3}}{2} kx, \tag{21W}$$

representing slightly *underdamped* oscillations of wave length

$$L_W = \frac{4\pi}{\sqrt{3}k} = \frac{4\pi}{\sqrt{3}\sqrt[3]{\beta}} A^{1/3}. \tag{24}$$

[2] The dependence $r(y)$ of the width of the ocean basin on latitude somewhat modifies this conclusion when applied to non-rectangular ocean basins (Munk and Carrier, 1950).

TABLE 1. Extrema of X_W and X'_W.

	Location (see fig. 3)			
	Western current axis	Western current limit	Countercurrent axis	Countercurrent limit
x/L_W	1/6	3/6	4/6	1
X_W	0.45	1.17	1.09	0.97
X'_W/k	0.55	0.00	−0.09	0.00

Table 1 gives the locations and values of the first few extrema. A remarkable feature is a countercurrent east[3] of the main current, whose magnitude is $\exp(-\pi/\sqrt{3})$, or 17 per cent of that of the main current. There can be little doubt that such countercurrents exist, although this fact has been obscured in some instances by the smoothing of data. In comparing the Kuroshio and the Gulf Stream, Wüst (1936, p. 56) remarks that (writer's translation) "... both currents are accompanied by a countercurrent on their right which attains surface velocities up to approximately 20 cm $\sec^{-1}$. This current, which is found for all Gulf Stream profiles based on *Atlantis* and *Dana* observations is a most peculiar phenomenon." According to Wüst's figures, the maximum speeds of the countercurrents average 19 per cent of that of the main currents, compared to the theoretical value of 17 per cent. In describing the Gulf Stream, Iselin (1936, p. 43) states that "... the western margin of the current is extremely abrupt, while on the eastern side the velocity decreases gradually." The theory places the current axis twice as near the western as the eastern side.

The function X_W (fig. 3) compares favorably with the transport function ψ (fig. 4) across the Gulf Stream and Kuroshio computed from oceanographic data according to the equations

$$\frac{f\psi}{\bar{\rho}} = Q = \int_{-h}^{z0} \int_{-h}^{p(z)} \delta' \, dp \, dz, \tag{25}$$

where δ' is the specific volume anomaly (Sverdrup *et al.*, 1942, p. 463), although there remain significant differences between the computed and observed transport curves, and of course between the observed currents themselves.

A review of oceanographic observations suggests 200 km and 250 km as typical values for the widths of the western currents and countercurrents, respectively. The corresponding values of A are 3.3×10^7

[3] A countercurrent on the *western* edge of the Gulf Stream has been accounted for by Rossby (1936) in his wake-stream theory. Further remarks will be found in section 10.

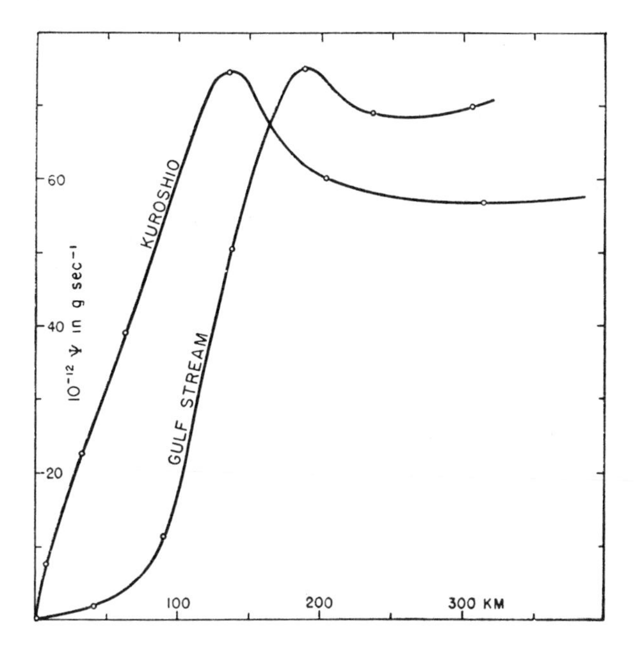

Fig. 4. The mass transport stream function ψ computed from oceanographic data across the Kuroshio and Gulf Stream. These curves should be compared to the theoretical function X on the left side of fig. 3. GULF STREAM: *Atlantis* stations 1225–1231, April 1932 (Iselin, 1936); $x = 0$ is placed at boundary between coastal water and slopewater. KUROSHIO: *Mansyu* stations 429–434, January 1927 (Wüst, 1936); $x = 0$ is placed at continental shelf.

and 6.5×10^7 cm² sec⁻¹ (equation 24), indicating perhaps an increase of A with distance from shore as might be expected on the basis of Prandtl's mixing-length theory. We shall set $A = 5 \times 10^7$ cm² sec⁻¹. This compares favorably with the values 4×10^7 and 7×10^7 cm² sec⁻¹ for the region of the Atlantic equatorial countercurrent, the former determined by Montgomery (1939) from the diffusion of salt, the latter by Montgomery and Palmén (1940) from dynamic principles. One may expect, however, that the value of A varies with time and location, and that for any fixed time and location it has different values, depending on the dimensions of the phenomenon under investigation. Without any further information we shall be obliged to consider the above value as constant.

The *total* transports of the western current and countercurrent are found by substituting values for X_W from table 1 into (22):

$$\psi_{WC} = -1.17 r \beta^{-1} \operatorname{curl}_z \boldsymbol{\tau}. \tag{26}$$

The resulting expressions *are independent of A*, and the transports can be computed with a relatively high degree of accuracy, being subject largely to uncertainties of the same order as those in computing wind stress. A comparison is made in table 2 between the transport values of some western currents determined from oceanographic observations, and those computed from the zonal wind stress according to (26). The effect of the meridional wind component, which supports the zonal winds, is introduced by a meridional wind factor (see section 7)

$$\overline{-\operatorname{curl}_z \boldsymbol{\tau}}\ (d\bar{\tau}_x/dy)^{-1}. \tag{27}$$

The approximation involved in permitting the "constants" β and r to assume different values at different latitudes implies that these vary slowly compared to $\boldsymbol{\tau}$ and ψ. However, not even a rapid change of r introduces an appreciable error into (26); the only essential modification is a widening and corresponding weakening of the western current, determined by the inclination of the western coastline relative to the assumed north–south direction (Munk and Carrier, 1950).

TABLE 2. The mass transport of some western currents determined from the wind stress (equation 26) and from oceanographic observations.

Current	Lat.	$10^{13}\,\beta$ cm^{-1} sec^{-1}	r km	$10^{10}\,\frac{d\tau_x}{dy}$ g sec^{-2}	Merid. wind factor	$10^{12}\,\psi$ Wind stress g sec^{-1}	$10^{12}\,\psi$ Oceanogr. g sec^{-1}
Gulf Stream	35°N	1.9	6,500	70	1.30	36	74[4] (55)[5]
Kuroshio Ext.	35°N	1.9	10,000	50	1.25	39	65[4]
Oyashio C.	50°N	1.5	5,500	−15	—	−6.5	−7[6]
Brazil C.	20°S	2.2	5,500	−20	—	−5.8	−5 to −10[4]

[4] Sverdrup *et al.* (1942), pp. 605–761.
[5] Adjusted for a supposed southward motion of 19 × 10^{12} g of slope water per second. Sverdrup *et al.* (1942), p. 679.
[6] For August (Uda, 1938).

The computed transport values differ from the observed values by as much as a factor of two, a discrepancy not surprising if one considers that, among other uncertainties, wind and current data are not for the same year, nor necessarily for the same time of year. On examining the possible sources of errors, one is led to ascribe some of the discrepancy to an underestimate of wind stress for low wind speeds. We shall return to this question in section 10.

The western boundary vortices (*Sargasso Sea*).—Beyond the countercurrent, the next term in (20) and (21) can no longer be neglected. It pivots the asymptotic solution $X = 1$ to $X = 1 - x/r$, and shifts $X'/k = 0$ to $X'/k = -1/kr$ (fig. 2, bottom). The resulting streamlines represent an exponentially decaying vortex trail centered along the axis φ_a (fig. 5). Only the two western vortices need be considered. Accordingly the Sargasso Sea (or any of the other dynamically analogous areas) is a region of relatively sluggish circulation containing a moderately strong anticyclonic vortex at the western side and a weak anticyclonic vortex near its center. The two vortices represent two humps in the sea surface which are separated by a trough with a saddle point in the vicinity of Bermuda. Reid's model (equation 23) gives 10 cm and 2 cm for the peak elevations of the western and eastern humps above the saddle point.

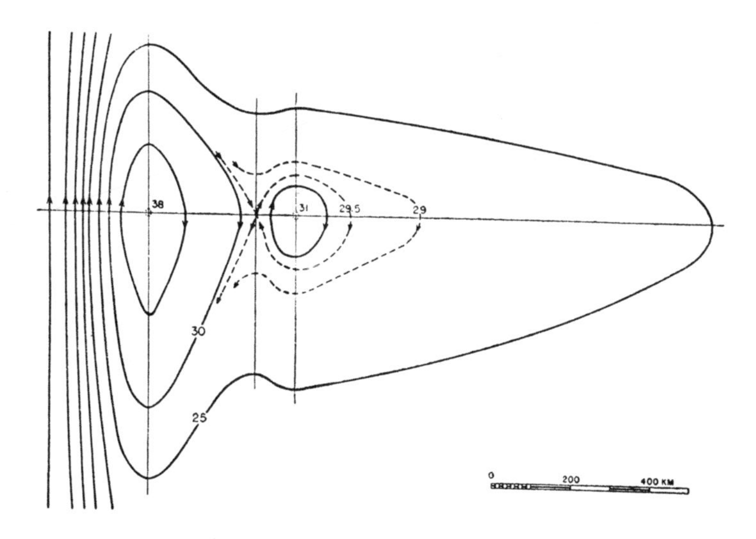

Fig. 5. The mass transport stream function in units of 10^{12} g sec^{-1} near the western boundary for mean annual zonal winds over the Atlantic. The center line is at 31°N. For comparison with the Sargasso Sea circulation, the figure should be distorted by maintaining the west–east orientation of the x-axis and rotating the y-axis clockwise until the western current and countercurrent are parallel to the coast line. (Munk and Carrier, 1950.)

Felber (1934) has analyzed the extensive observational material based on surface drifts of vessels, and his streamlines show a saddle point southwest of Bermuda. A chart of the topography of the sea surface prepared by Defant (1941) on the basis of the *Meteor* observations and preceding observations, does indeed show two humps. Recent detailed observations from closely spaced lowerings of bathythermographs, though inconclusive, are not inconsistent with the above picture

Central ocean drift.—Away from both boundaries, the equations

$$X_C = 1 - x/r, \qquad X'_C/k = -1/kr, \qquad \text{(20C, 21C)}$$

$$M_y = \partial\psi/\partial x = \beta^{-1}\,\mathrm{curl}_z\,\boldsymbol{\tau} \qquad (28)$$

give a broad *constant* drift that compensates for the swift, shallow western currents. Equation (28) was derived by Sverdrup (1947). By dropping the lateral stress term this equation could have been written directly from (6) *without the restriction to zonal winds.* The validity of the theory in mid-ocean has been adequately confirmed by the successful application of (28) to the equatorial currents of the eastern Pacific (Sverdrup, 1947; Reid, 1948a, b).

Eastern coastal strip.—The eastern solution

$$X_E = 1 - \frac{x}{r} - \frac{1}{kr}\left[1 - e^{-k(r-x)}\right], \qquad \text{(20E)}$$

$$\frac{X'_E}{k} = -\frac{1}{kr}\left[1 - e^{-k(r-x)}\right] \qquad \text{(21E)}$$

represents an exponential slippage zone of width, say, π/k (fig. 3). For $A = 5 \times 10^7$ cm^2 sec^{-1} this corresponds to roughly 200 km. This feature is likely to be obscured by meridional wind currents (section 6).

The west-east asymmetry.—The westward intensification of ocean currents[7] has been explained by Stommel (1948) as related to the planetary vorticity. The asymmetry may be expressed as either of the ratios

$$\frac{M_y(WC)}{M_y(C)} = -0.55kr; \qquad \frac{r}{x(WC)} = \frac{\sqrt{3}}{2\pi}kr$$

[7] Dynamically it is perhaps more significant to consider the concentration of virtually all the oceans' vorticity against their western shores.

of the maximum western current to the central drift, or of the width of the ocean to that of the western current. The asymmetry increases with r, decreases with A and φ. For the Atlantic we found $kr \approx 100$.

But the asymmetry is not only one of narrow swift currents versus broad slow currents. The countercurrent and opposing vortices are part of the western dynamic pattern for which there is no counterpart on the eastern side of the oceans. The equivalent mathematical statement is that the real parts of the two complex roots α_1 and α_2 of the characteristic equations (16) are always negative, whereas the real roots α_3 and α_4 are positive. The leftward trend in fig. 1 of α_1' and α_2' with increasing γ shows that the asymmetry becomes even more pronounced for large zonal wind wave-numbers.

These remarks can be interpreted in terms of the differential equation of mass transport (equation 6):

$$\underbrace{\text{Lateral stress curl} + \overbrace{\text{planetary vorticity}}^{} }_{\text{western solution}} \! \phantom{\text{planetary vorticity}} + \text{wind stress curl} = 0.$$

$$\underbrace{\text{planetary vorticity} + \text{wind stress curl}}_{\text{central solution}}$$

In the central and eastern ocean areas the planetary vorticity and wind stress curl have opposite signs, and balance is achieved in which the lateral stress plays a negligible part (except in the unimportant eastern coastal zone). Along the western boundary the planetary vorticity and wind stress curl have the same sign, and the lateral stress curl balances both planetary vorticity and wind stress curl.[8] It can be verified that in this region the wind stress curl is *numerically* unimportant, although it is of course the primary cause of the circulation. The above remarks apply not only to both hemispheres, but also to the cyclonic as well as the anticyclonic gyres. The only way in which the intense currents and the boundary vortices could occur on the eastern side of the oceans would be for the earth to rotate in the opposite sense.

5. MERIDIONAL WIND SOLUTION

Superimposed on the eastern drift we find in various oceans rather well developed currents along the eastern boundary, the Benguela, California, Peru and Alaska currents being the outstanding examples.

[8] Stockmann (1946) has given a formal solution to (8); that is, he has neglected the important planetary vorticity.

These currents are seasonal and vary with the winds. Since they are not contained in our solution for a zonal wind circulation we must assume that they depend on the vorticity provided by the meridional winds.

The procedure to be followed is similar to the one in section (3). The meridional wind stress in the interval $0 < x < r$ will be written as a sum of terms $\tau_{ym} = a \cos mx + b \sin mx + c$, where $m = j\pi/r$, $j = 1, 2, \cdots$ *etc.* Neglecting the effects of northern and southern boundaries, $\psi = \psi(x)$, and equation (6) reduces to

$$\left(A \frac{d^4}{dx^4} - \beta \frac{d}{dx}\right) \psi_m = - \text{curl}_{zm} \boldsymbol{\tau} = - \frac{d\tau_{ym}}{dx}. \tag{6M}$$

The general solution for the mth component of ψ is

$$\psi_m = \frac{\tau_{ym} - \dfrac{\delta_m^3}{m}\dfrac{d\tau_{ym}}{dx}}{k^3A(1 + \delta_m^6)} + e^{-\frac{1}{2}kx}\left[q_1 \cos\left(\frac{\sqrt{3}}{2}kx - q_2\right) + q_3 + q_4 e^{-k(r-x)}\right], \tag{15M}$$

where $\delta_m = m/k$ is the ratio between the meridional wind stress wave number m and the Coriolis-friction wave number $k = \sqrt[3]{\beta/A}$, and the q's are constants to be determined from the four boundary conditions (9).

In the central and eastern ocean areas ($e^{-\frac{1}{2}kx} \ll 1$) for a relatively broad meridional wind system ($\delta \ll 1$) equation (15M) gives

$$\psi(x) = \beta^{-1}[(\tau_y)_x - (\tau_y)_r + k^{-1}(\text{curl}_z \boldsymbol{\tau})_r(1 - e^{-k(r-x)})], \tag{29}$$

$$M_y(x) = \beta^{-1}[(\text{curl}_z \boldsymbol{\tau})_x - (\text{curl}_z \boldsymbol{\tau})_r e^{-k(r-x)}], \tag{30}$$

independent of the wave-number m. Beyond the eastern coastal strip, (30) reduces again to Sverdrup's equation (28).

6. THE CALIFORNIA CURRENT SYSTEM

Off the coast of California, perhaps as a consequence of the coastal mountain range, the usual situation is for the summer winds south of Cape Mendocino (the *Cape Horn of California*) to blow from NNW and to reach their maximum speed some distance from shore (fig. 6). Along this wind axis the curl of the wind stress changes sign, and, neglecting the very small last term in (30), the direction of transport changes sign also. The existence of this biologically important counter-

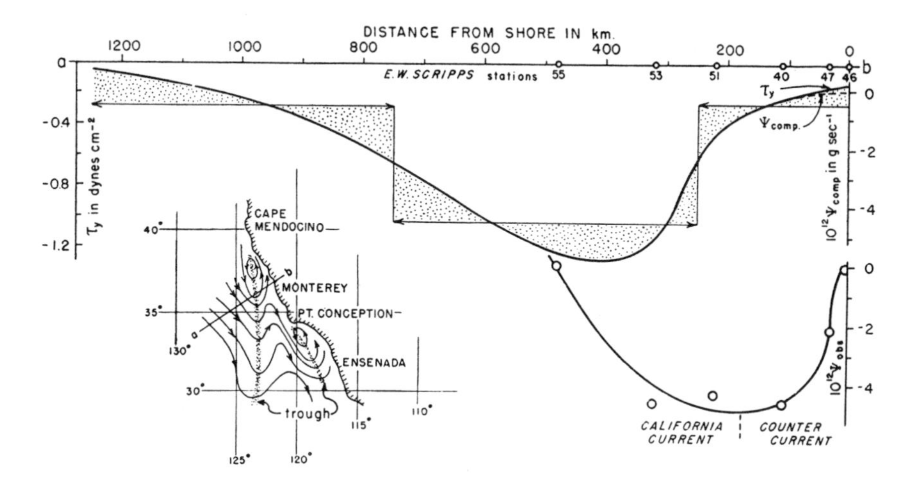

Fig. 6. Meridional winds and currents off California. Horizontal arrows in upper figure show average values of τ_y (left scale) for June over the indicated ranges along section a–b, inset. The solid curve is a rough estimate of the actual wind distribution. Except for a narrow region near shore where a slight modification is introduced by the last term in equation (30), this curve represents also the computed mass transport (right scale). The mass transport above the 1000-decibar level from oceanographic observations (Sverdrup and staff, 1942) according to equation (25) is shown by the lower curve. The inset shows dynamic height anomalies, 0 over 1000 decibar, based on observations of the *E. W. Scripps* cruise VIII, 10 May to 10 July 1939.

current is confirmed by an oceanographic section off Monterey occupied by the *E. W. Scripps* on 11–14 June 1939 (fig. 6). The width of the current during this cruise appeared to have been considerably narrower than would be consistent with average June winds. The total transport of the countercurrent according to (29) is about 6×10^{12} g sec^{-1}; according to the oceanographic data, 5×10^{12} g sec^{-1}.

The boundary between the California Current and countercurrent represents a trough in the sea surface (inset, fig. 6) which corresponds to the axis of the northerly winds. Off the coast of Mexico, both the trough and wind axis are located further offshore. A second trough associated with an eddy south of Pt. Conception appears to be related to a second maximum of the northerly winds extending from Pt. Conception in a line with San Nicolas Island.

The foregoing application of the meridional solution suffers from the limited extent of the wind system and the lack of adequate meteorologic and oceanographic observations. All that can be said is that the average wind distribution off Monterey is consistent with the existence of a south-flowing current offshore and a countercurrent inshore, and that the computed transports of these currents compare favorably with the measured transports. It should be noted that this current-countercurrent system is a consequence of the *local* wind stress curl and dynamically altogether different from the current-countercurrent system along the western side of the oceans, which has been interpreted as a boundary phenomenon.

7. GENERAL SOLUTION

Consider now the general field of wind stress

$$\boldsymbol{\tau} = \mathbf{i}\tau_x(x, y) + \mathbf{j}\tau_y(x, y)$$

associated with large-scale atmospheric circulation, *i.e.*, $\gamma \ll 1$, $\delta \ll 1$. Outside the western and eastern boundary regions, (6) then has the integral

$$\psi_C = -rX_C\beta^{-1}\,\overline{\text{curl}_z\,\boldsymbol{\tau}},$$

where X_C is given by (20C), and

$$\overline{\text{curl}_z\,\boldsymbol{\tau}} = \frac{1}{r - x}\int_x^r \text{curl}_z\,\boldsymbol{\tau}\,dx \tag{31}$$

represents a *running* average along a segment of latitude between x and the eastern boundary. If variations of the wind stress curl with x in the western and eastern boundary regions are so gradual that ψ fluctuates essentially with $X(x)$, then

$$\psi = -rX\beta^{-1}\,\overline{\text{curl}_z\,\boldsymbol{\tau}} \tag{32}$$

is a suitable approximation for the entire ocean area. The above condition requires $m \ll k$, which is true by hypothesis. It is in the nature of the (running) average $\overline{\text{curl}_z\,\boldsymbol{\tau}}$ that it should become the less effected by local fluctuations in the wind field the larger the value of $r - x$. This must be at least a partial explanation for the known persistency of zonal currents in the western portion of all oceans.

8. THE WIND-SPUN VORTEX

For a stationary, anticyclonic, circular wind system

$$\tau_\rho = 0, \qquad \tau_\theta = -\Gamma q\rho e^{-q^2\rho^2}, \tag{33}$$

reaching a maximum stress $\Gamma/\sqrt{2e}$ at a distance from the center $\rho = \frac{1}{2}\sqrt{2}\, q^{-1}$ and zero stress at the center and at great distances, the stream function in the central ocean area (equation 20C, 31, 32) becomes

$$\psi = \beta^{-1} \int_x^\infty \text{curl}_z\, \tau\, dx = \tfrac{1}{2}\sqrt{\pi}\Gamma\beta^{-1}\{[1 - 2(qy)^2][1 - I] + \tfrac{1}{2}I''\}, \quad (34)$$

where

$$I(q\rho) = \frac{2}{\sqrt{\pi}} \int_0^{q\rho} e^{-(q\rho)^2}\, d(q\rho)$$

is the probability integral and $I'' = d^2I/d(q\rho)^2$. It is assumed that the wind system essentially vanishes some distance from shore.

The mass-transport streamlines (fig. 7) reveal an anticyclonic vortex centered at $-1/q$, 0, and a trough with a saddle point at $1/q$, 0. The center of the oceanic vortex is thus displaced *west* from the center of the atmospheric vortex by $\sqrt{2}$ times the radius of the

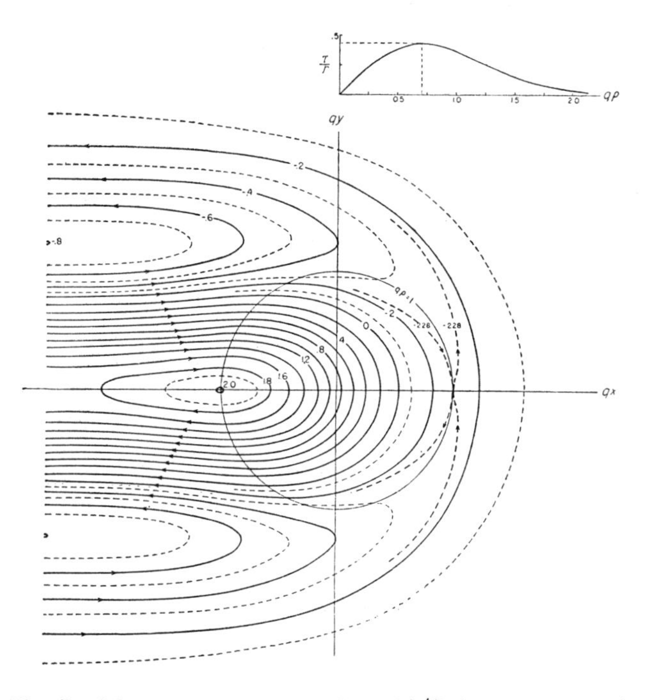

Fig. 7. Mass transport stream lines $\beta\psi/\Gamma$ (nondimensional) resulting from the circular wind system shown above.

maximum stress circle. The net anticyclonic circulation in the vortex is $(2.0 + .228)\Gamma/\beta = 5.2\tau_{max}/\beta$.

Meteorologic and oceanic observations in the eastern Pacific definitely show a westward displacement of the oceanic anticyclone relative to the Pacific high-pressure area with which it is associated. The magnitudes of the displacement ($\approx$1000 km) and the circulation ($\approx 20 \times 10^{12}$ g sec^{-1}) are about 60 per cent of what one might suppose on the basis of the foregoing theory. However, the lack of radial symmetry of the wind system because of its poor development in the western portion prevents a more quantitative application of the theory. The oceanographic observations are inadequate to either confirm or deny the existence of the saddle point.

It should be noticed that ψ vanishes at $x = +\infty$ but not at $x = -\infty$. This is the result of having neglected the lateral stress vorticity in dealing with the first-order equation (28) which admits only one boundary condition. For large anticyclones ($q/k \ll 1$), fig. 7 should be a good mid-ocean approximation, and one may expect a *tail* of predominately zonal currents west of the wind system, feeding water into the system north of the wind axis and expelling it south of the wind axis (vice versa for cyclones), with relatively weak compensation currents farther to the north and south. The effect of lateral stress will be to shorten the tail in proportion to the compactness of the wind system. For a wind system consisting of alternate cyclonic and anticyclonic cells over the entire globe, Goldsbrough (1935) finds a current system of similar cellular structure but displaced westward relative to the wind cells.

9. CLASSIFICATION OF OCEAN CURRENTS

In writing this paper we have felt an increasing need for a general nomenclature of ocean currents, applicable in all oceans regardless of hemisphere, and suggestive of the meteorologic features to which the currents are so closely related. A possible system is proposed in fig. 8. The corresponding geographic names for all oceans are summarized in table 3. The circulation is divided into gyres, which are equivalent in scale to the climatic belts. Each gyre contains one or two *vortices* equivalent in scale to semipermanent pressure centers. It is suggested that the term *eddy* be reserved for random features associated with turbulence.

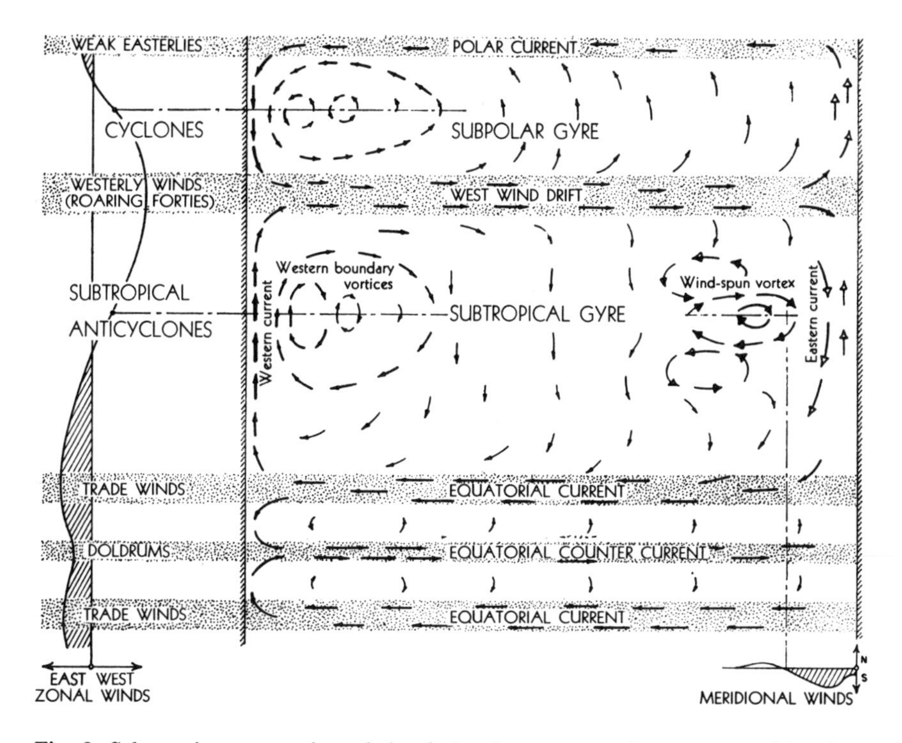

Fig. 8. Schematic presentation of circulation in a rectangular ocean resulting from zonal winds (filled arrowheads), meridional winds (open arrowheads), or both (half-filled arrowheads). The width of the arrows is an indication of the strength of the currents. The nomenclature applies to either hemisphere, but in the Southern Hemisphere the subpolar gyre is replaced largely by the Antarctic Circumpolar Current (west wind drift) flowing around the world. Geographic names of the currents in various oceans are summarized in table 3.

In high (north or south) latitudes the cyclonic *subpolar* gyre corresponds to the region of the cyclonic storms, the anticyclonic *subtropical* gyre to the anticyclones. The equatorial currents and countercurrent enclose two additional gyres (see fig. 2) corresponding to the trades and the doldrums, but these are so narrow that they are best not regarded as gyres. A typcal gyre is composed of zonal currents to the north and south, a strong persistent current and boundary vortex on its western side, and a compensating drift in the central and eastern portion, upon which a variable eastern current and wind-spun vortex are superimposed.

The foregoing classification has chemical and biological implications (see charts IV and VI, figs. 217, 216, and 214, Sverdrup *et al.*, 1942). The subtropical gyres, for example, enclose a relatively warm,

TABLE 3. The general ocean circulation

Gyre	Classification (see fig. 8)		North Atlantic	South Atlantic
Subpolar Gyre	POLAR CURRENT	(z)		p ?
			E. Greenland (3)	
	Western C.	(z)	Labrador (6) ?	Falkland
	W. bdry vortex	(z)	p ? (50°N, 50°W)	a ?
	Eastern C.	(m)	Norwegian (3)	a
	Wind-spun vortex	(z, m)	a	a ?
	WEST WIND DRIFT	(z)	Gulf Stream S.: N. Atlantic (38)	West wind drift
Subtropical Gyre			Gulf Stream S.: Gulf Stream (70)	
	Western C.	(z)		Brazil (7)
			Gulf Stream S.: Florida (26)	
	W. bdry vortex	(z)	Gulf Stream S.: Sargasso Sea	p
	Eastern C.	(m)	Canary ?	Benguela (16)
	Wind-spun vortex	(z, m)	Azores vortex	p (30°S, 5°W)
	EQUATORIAL CURRENT	(z)	N. Equat. C. (32)	S. Equat. C.
	EQUAT. COUNTER C.	(z)	Equat. C. C. (4)	← a

a: absent; p: present, but unnamed; m: related to meridional winds; S: system; v: variable; w: weak; z: related to zonal winds.

TABLE 3.—continued

	North Pacific	South Pacific	North Indian	South Indian
	p	p (w)		p
	Oyashio	a		a
	?	a		a
	Alaska	a		a
			A	
	Gulf of Alaska	a		a
			S	
	Aleutian (15)			
			I	
			A	
KUROSHIO S.	N. Pacific (20)	West wind drift		West wind drift
	Kuroshio Ext. (65)			
	Kuroshio (23)	E. Australia ?		Agulhas (25)
	p	p		p
	California (15)	Peru (13)		p (v)
	E. Pac. vortex	p (30°S, 100°W)		p (30°S, 95°E)
	N. Equat. C. (45)	S. Equat. C.	N. Equat. C.	S. Equat. C.
	Equat. C. C. (25)	⟵ a	a ⟶	Equat. C. C.

Figures in parentheses give mass transport in 10^{12} g sec^{-1} estimated from oceanographic observations.

haline body of water, poor in phosphates, relatively low in biological activity, and blue in color ('blue is the desert color of the sea'). The boundaries of the gyres are marked by remarkably pronounced horizontal gradients in all these variables. The western boundary vortices are biologically unique in that they represent the only regions in the open sea where freely floating organisms in the sunlit zone can be expected to remain for any length of time in a uniform environment. Of such regions, named *halostases* by biologists, the best known is the Sargasso Sea, named after its concentration of *Sargassum*, or *Gulf Weed*, a brown alga characteristic of subtropical regions. The six remaining halostases (table 3) are equivalent dynamically to the Sargasso Sea and it would not be surprising were they also distinguished by concentrations of freely floating organisms with narrow environmental tolerance.

10. DISCUSSION AND CONCLUSIONS

The classification of ocean currents in table 3 is put forth with some hesitation, as it is almost certain to include some unwarranted over-simplification. Additional data on currents and wind stress are likely to lead to revisions. Particularly in the southern oceans the boundary conditions for the subpolar gyre differ radically from those we have considered, and the dynamics of the Antarctic Circumpolar Current is not properly understood. But even so, a preliminary table is helpful in interpreting the main features in the ocean circulation and, what is more important, to point out reasons for essential *differences* in different oceans.

For example, the Gulf Stream and Brazil Current occupy equivalent positions in the North and South Atlantic, yet the Gulf Stream has about ten times as much transport. According to (26) and table 2 this difference is due chiefly to the larger wind stress curl in the North Atlantic. Differences in wind stress curl can be ascribed to the northward displacement of the climatic equator relative to the geographical equator, which reduces the distance between the trades and the westerlies in the northern hemisphere to about 60 per cent of that in the southern hemisphere. The displacement of the trades in turn seems to be related to the unequal distribution of land and sea in the two hemispheres. One is tempted, then, to trace the preponderance of the great Gulf Stream and Kuroshio systems over their southern counterpart to the excess of water-covered area in the southern hemisphere.

Differences in circulation between the North Atlantic and North Pacific can be at least partly ascribed to the greater intensity and northward displacement of the Atlantic zonal winds, especially during winter (fig. 9). The circulation in the subpolar gyre of the North Atlantic is complicated by two related factors: both the northern land boundaries and the axis of the westerly winds are further north in the eastern than the central and western portion. This may be the reason why the western current of the subpolar gyre is broken up into two parts (Sverdrup *et al.*, 1942, pp. 651–666): the East-Greenland current flowing at an average longitude of 30°W from 80°N to 60°N; and the Labrador current at 60°W, flowing from 60°N to 40°N.

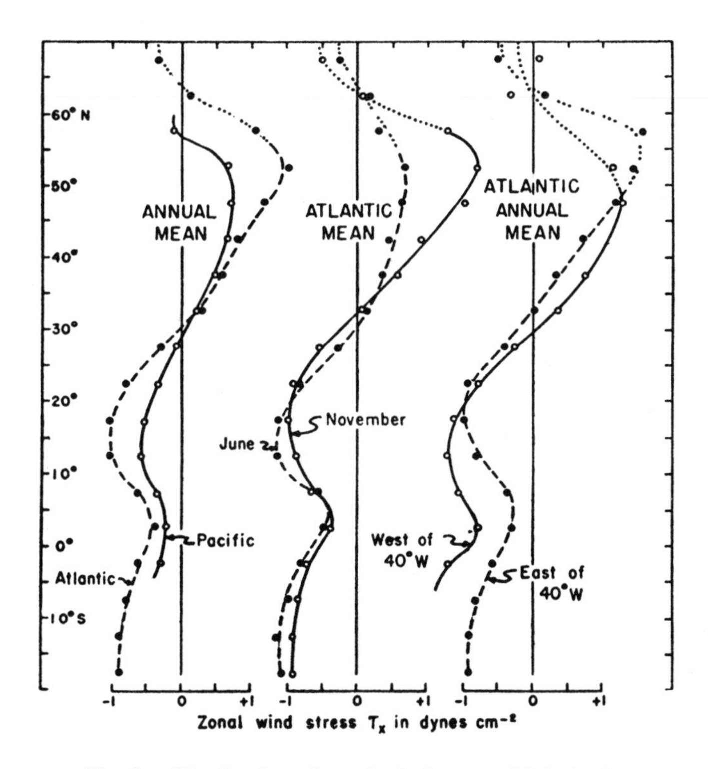

Fig. 9. Distribution of zonal wind stress with latitude. Note the longitudinal asymmetry over the North Atlantic. In the region south of Greenland, where observations are lacking, the wind stress averages have been corrected for this asymmetry. The dotted lines indicate uncertainty because of lack of sufficient observational data.

The wind stress pattern over the subpolar gyre is largely a reflection of the traveling cyclones, and one may expect a certain adjustment of the ocean circulation to the frequency and paths of these cyclones. The extent of such an adjustment depends on the time constants of the ocean circulation. Observational evidence indicates that the adjustment to individual storms is not a major one, yet that the main currents do reveal seasonal fluctuations. The time constants appear, therefore, to be of the order of weeks, perhaps months. Thus ocean currents might represent a convenient method of obtaining time averages of atmospheric circulation. For example, the intensity of the Gulf Stream (perhaps estimated from tide records) could be related to the mean wind vorticity in the region of subtropical anticyclones over the Atlantic.

The foregoing statement is somewhat at variance with the usual assertion that the Gulf Stream is *caused* by the trades. Rather it is related to the vector *difference* between the trades and the westerlies, or, strictly speaking, to the mean value of the wind stress curl at the latitude in question. It is at least conceivable that an increase in the velocity of the trades be confined to a narrow band of latitude, and that the wind stress curl and the Gulf Stream at, say, 30°N remain unchanged. This is, however, unlikely for physical reasons as the mechanism responsible for the transfer of momentum from the westerlies to the trades would tend to distribute such an increase over the entire subtropical zone.

The validity of our statement that the intensity of the western current be proportional to the wind stress curl at the latitude in question depends on the approximations involved in neglecting the inertial terms in (1). Rossby (1936) has developed a *wake-stream theory* of the Gulf Stream in which the inertial terms play a predominant part. The theory has many attractive features. It explains the increase downstream in width and mass transport, the existence of an observed countercurrent on the *western* edge of the Gulf Stream, and a jet-like current profile which appears to be in accord with recent observations (Iselin and Fuglister, 1948).

In order to estimate the magnitude of the inertial terms it is necessary to specify the distribution of density and velocity with depth. Using Reid's exponential model for the density (23) and a similar law for the velocity:

$$v = v_0 \text{ for } -z \leqslant h', \qquad v = v_0 e^{1+z'1/h} \text{ for } -z \geqslant h',$$

one obtains the expression

$$\frac{3}{8}\frac{1}{\rho_0 h'}\nabla \times (\mathbf{M}\cdot\nabla)\mathbf{M}, \tag{35}$$

to be added to the left side of the differential equation of mass transport (6). The ratio

$$\frac{\sqrt{3}}{4}\frac{rk^2n^2\tau_{\max}}{\rho_0 h'\beta^2}\,e^{-\frac{1}{2}kx}\cos\left(\frac{\sqrt{3}}{2}kx + \frac{\pi}{6}\right), \tag{36}$$

of (35) to the planetary vorticity is small except along the inshore edge of the western current, where it may reach unity. It seems likely that some of our conclusions will be modified in the sense prescribed by Rossby.

This investigation has served to emphasize the fundamental importance of the wind stress *curl* rather than of the wind stress *vector* in determining the transport of ocean currents in meridionally bounded oceans. For example, the circulation shown in figs. 2 and 6 is in no ways modified by shifting the zero axis of the wind stress curve. It so happens that in the subtropical zone the inflection point of the zonal wind stress curve falls close to where the wind stress changes sign, and it has been tacitly assumed in most textbooks that the change from a westward to an eastward current is related to a similar change in wind direction. This general misconception probably explains the difficulty in interpreting instances where the current runs against the wind, such as the California Countercurrent, the Point Barrow Current, and most important of all, the Equatorial Countercurrent. In the case of an irrotational wind field, such as a uniform west wind, over an ocean bounded on its western and eastern sides, it follows from (4) and (22) that $\psi = 0$, $\nabla P = \boldsymbol{\tau}$, *i.e.*, that there is no circulation and that the stress is balanced by the pressure distribution resulting from the piling up of water against the lee shore. With the important exception of the Antarctic Circumpolar Current, which has no major meridional boundaries, it can be stated that *permanent ocean currents are related to the rotational component of the wind stress field over the ocean. These ocean currents would vanish were the wind stress field irrotational.*

Finally we may examine the question of why the computed transports of the Gulf Stream and the Kuroshio current amount to only about one half the observed values (table 2). It does not seem reasonable that the oceanographic observations should be off by more than, say, 20 per cent, nor that the theoretical expression (26) for the transport should account for the discrepancy, since it is almost independent of the eddy viscosity and the shape of the ocean basin.

Maury and others have ascribed the North Atlantic circulation, in particular the Gulf Stream, to differential heating between equator and pole, to the freezing of ice, and to other processes that make up the *thermohaline* circulation. If we assume that the circulation were half wind-driven, half thermohaline, it would be a strange coincidence that the general *pattern* of the circulation, such as the boundaries of the gyres, should conform so closely to the general atmospheric circulation. Furthermore, Fuglister[9] has found a high correlation between *variations* in the current with variations in the wind. It should also be noted that the thermohaline circulation insofar as it is related to the outflow of river water along the Atlantic seaboard would tend to reduce rather than to strengthen the Gulf Stream. It would seem therefore that the subtropical gyre, and probably also the subpolar gyre, are predominantly wind-driven.

Methods for computing wind stress from the observed wind speeds according to the equation

$$\tau = C_D \rho_{\mathrm{air}} U^2$$

are discussed by Reid (1948a) and in SIO Oceanographic Report 14.[10] Underestimates of τ may first of all result from underestimates in the wind speeds on the climatological charts from which the appropriate averages were taken. The preponderance of coastal stations, and the tendency of ships at sea to avoid regions of high wind, would lead to consistent errors, but these cannot account for more than a fraction of the discrepancies. The weakest link is the drag coefficient C_D which is based on measurements of Baltic storm tides, and a few other measurements (Sverdrup *et al.*, 1942, pp. 489–500). In accordance with the views presently accepted we have assumed $C_D = .0026$ at high wind speeds, $C_D \approx .008$ at low speeds, with the discontinuity occurring at Beaufort 4 (Munk, 1947). In the tradewind belt of the eastern Pacific, where the winds are predominantly Beaufort 4 and above, Sverdrup (1947) and Reid (1948a) have obtained satisfactory agreement between computed and observed transports. Supposing a value of .0026 were applicable at all wind speeds,

[9] F. C. Fuglister, "Annual variations in current speeds in the Gulf Stream system," *Woods Hole Oceanographic Institution Technical Report No. 15* (unpublished), 1948.

[10] Scripps Institution of Oceanography, "The field of mean wind stress over the North Pacific Ocean," Oceanographic Report No. 14 (unpublished).

then the effect of the southwesterly winds over the eastern Atlantic would make itself felt in a much higher meridional wind factor (table 2), and it can be demonstrated that the discrepancy between computed and observed transports could be largely accounted for. We are therefore led to propose a higher value of C_D at low wind speeds.[11] The transports of the Gulf Stream and Kuroshio current are, after all, probably as good an indicator of the overall stress exerted by the winds on the ocean as any of the measurements on which the value of C_D is now based.

Acknowledgments.—The writer has benefited greatly by many discussion with Einar Hiøland of the Institute of Theoretical Astrophysics, University of Oslo, where most of this paper was prepared. Drs. H. U. Sverdrup, C.-G. Rossby and C. E. Eckart have made many helpful suggestions. The tedious computations of wind stress have been performed by Jo Nixon and Viola Bush under the supervision of Robert Reid, John Cochrane and Palmer Osborn, as part of a research project sponsored by the Office of Naval Research. The writer is also deeply indebted to the Guggenheim Foundation for its generous support.

References

Defant, A., 1941: Die absolute Topographie des physikalischen Meeresniveaus und der Druckflachen, sowie die Wasserbewegungen im Atlantischen Ozean. *Deutsche Atlantische Expedition METEOR 1925–1927, Wiss. Erg.*, **6,** No. 2/5, fig. 41.

Ekman, V. W., 1923: Uber Horizontalzirkulation bei winderzeugten Meeresstromungen. *Arkiv Mat. Astr. Fysik,* **17,** No. 26, 74 pp.

Ekman, V. W., 1932: Studien zur Dynamik der Meeresstromungen. *Gerlands Beitr. Geophysik,* **36,** 385–438.

Felbert, O-H., 1934: Oberflachenstromungen des Nordatlantischen Ozeans zwischen 15° and 50°N.B. *Arch. Deutschen Seewarte,* **53,** 2–50.

Goldsbrough, G. R., 1935: On ocean currents produced by winds. *Proc. roy. Soc. London.* (A), **148,** 47–58.

Hidaka, K., 1949: Mass transport in ocean currents and lateral mixing. *J. marine Res.*, **8,** 1932–36.

Iselin, C. O'D., 1936: A study of the circulation of the western North Atlantic. *Pap. phys. Ocean. Meteor., Mass. Inst. Tech. and Woods Hole ocean Instn.*, **4,** No. 4, 101 pp.

Iselin, C. O'D., and F. C. Fuglister, 1948: Some recent developments in the study of the Gulf Stream. *J. Marine Res.*, **7,** 317–329. (Sverdrup Anniv. Vol.)

[11] Neumann (1948) claims on the basis of his analysis of Baltic and North Sea tilt that the drag coefficient actually *increases* with decreasing wind speed. His average value for C_D pertaining to Beaufort 3 is in excess of .0040.

Love, A. E. H., 1944: *A treatise on the mathematical theory of elasticity.* Fourth Ed., Dover, New York, 643 pp.

Montgomery, R. B., 1939: Ein Versuch, den vertikalen und seitlichen Austausch in der Tiefe der Sprungschichte im äquatorialen Atlantischen Ozean zu bestimmen. *Ann. Hydrogr. mar. Meteor.*, **67,** 242–246.

Munk, W. H., and G. F. Carrier, 1950: The wind-driven circulation in ocean basins of various shapes. *Tellus* (in press).

Munk, W. H., 1947: A critical wind speed for air-sea boundary processes. *J. Marine Res.*, **6,** 203–218.

Neumann, G., 1948: Uber den Tangentialdruck des Windes und die Rauhigkeit der Meeresoberflache. *Z. f. Meteor.*, **2,** 193–203.

Rayleigh, Lord, 1893: On the flow of viscous fluids, especially in two dimensions. *Phil. Mag.* (5), **36,** 354–372.

Reid, R. O., 1948a: The equatorial currents of the eastern Pacific as maintained by the stress of the wind. *J. Marine Res.*, **7,** 74–99.

Reid, R. O., 1948b: A model of the vertical structure of mass in equatorial wind-driven currents of a baroclinic ocean. *J. Marine Res.*, **7,** 304–312. (Sverdrup Anniv. Vol.)

Rossby, C.-C., 1936: Dynamics of steady ocean currents in the light of experimental fluid mechanics. *Pap. phys. Ocean. Meteor., Mass. Inst. Tech. & Woods Hole ocean. Instn.*, **5,** No. 1, 43 pp.

Stockmann, W. B., 1946: Equations for a field of total flow induced by the wind in a non-homogeneous sea. *C. R. Acad. Sci. URSS.*, **54,** 403–406.

Stommel, H., 1948: The westward intensification of wind-driven ocean currents. *Trans. Amer. geophys. Union*, **29,** 202–206.

Sverdrup, H. U., and staff, 1942: Oceanographic observations on the "E. W. Scripps" cruises of 1938. *Records of observations*, Scripps Inst. Ocean., **1,** 1–64.

Sverdrup, H. U., M. W. Johnson, and R. H. Fleming, 1942: *The Oceans, their physics, chemistry, and general biology.* Prentice-Hall, New York, 1087 pp.

Sverdrup, H. U., 1947: Wind-driven currents in a baroclinic ocean; with application to the equatorial currents of the eastern Pacific. *Proc. Nat. Acad. Sci.*, **33,** 318–326.

Uda, M., 1938: Hydrographical fluctuation in the northeastern sea-region adjacent to Japan of North Pacific Ocean. *Japan, Imper. Fisheries Sta., Jour.*, **9,** 64–85.

Wüst, G., 1936: Kuroshio and Golfstrom. *Berlin Univ., Inst. f. Meereskunde, Veröff., N. F.*, A. Geogr.-Naturwiss., **29,** 69 pp.

The wind-driven circulation in ocean basins of various shapes

W. H. Munk and G. F. Carrier

Reprinted with permission from Tellus
Volume 2, Number 3,
pages 158 through 167, 1950

The Wind-driven Circulation in Ocean Basins of Various Shapes

By W. H. MUNK[1] and G. F. CARRIER[2]

(Manuscript received 6 March 1950)

Abstract

The ocean circulation induced by zonal winds has been derived for a triangular ocean basin. The method, which involves the "boundary layer" technique, can be extended to a more general wind system, and to ocean basins of arbitrary shape provided the boundaries are not too irregular. In low and mid-latitudes the principal effect of an inclination, Θ, of the western boundary relative to a north-south direction is to widen the western current (Gulf Stream) by the factor $(\sec \Theta)^{1/3}$ and to reduce the current intensity by a similar factor. A variation in the circulation pattern associated with the variation in the value of the lateral eddy viscosity is noted.

Introduction

The wind-driven circulation in a rectangular ocean basin has been discussed by HIDAKA (1949) and by one of us.[3] The actual shapes of the North Atlantic and North Pacific Oceans deviate greatly from that of a rectangle, but resemble somewhat more closely triangular or semicircular basins, the two cases considered in this paper. The solutions obtained indicate the effect on western currents, such as the Gulf Stream and Kuroshio, of the orientation and curvature of the coast line.

The equation of mass transport and boundary conditions

The stream lines of mass transport, ψ, obey the equation (WOC)

$$\left(A\Delta^4 - \beta\frac{\partial}{\partial x}\right)\psi = -\operatorname{curl}_z\tau, \qquad (1)$$

where A is the kinematic eddy viscosity pertaining to lateral stresses, $\nabla^4 = \partial^4/\partial x^4 + 2\partial^4/\partial x^2\partial y^2 + \partial^4/\partial y^4$ is the biharmonic operator,

$$\beta = \frac{df}{dy} = \frac{2\Omega}{R}\cos\varphi \qquad (2)$$

is the rate of change northward (positive y) of twice the vertical component of the earth's angular velocity Ω, f the Coriolis parameter, R the earth's radius, φ latitude, and $\operatorname{curl}_z\tau$ the vertical component of the wind stress curl. The positive x-axis extends eastward.

Equation (1) is essentially an integrated version of the vorticity equation, and expresses a balance between three torques: the lateral stress torque, the planetary vorticity, and the wind curl. The equation has been derived (WOC) by integrating the equations of motion (including horizontal and vertical turbulent stresses) from the surface to some depth where the motion and horizontal pressure gradients essentially vanish, and then performing the curl operation. Observations have shown that the velocity of the wind-driven currents at depths of one or two thousand meters equals but a small fraction of the surface velocity.

---

[1] Institute of Geophysics and Scripps Institution of Oceanography, University of California. Contribution from the Scripps Institution of Oceanography, New Series, No. 483. This work has been supported by the Office of Naval Research.

[2] Department of Applied Mathematics, Brown University, Providence, Rhode Island.

[3] W. H. MUNK (1950), *On the Wind-driven Ocean Circulation*, published in the Journal of Meteorology. This article will hereafter be referred to by the symbol (WOC).

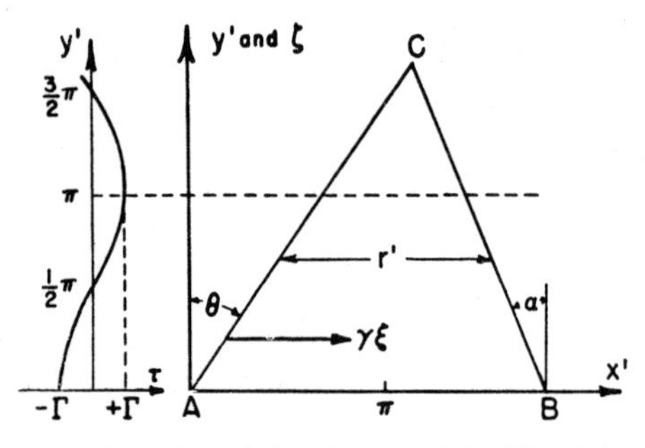

Fig. 1. Dimensions of triangular ocean basin. The wind stress τ varies from $-\Gamma$ at $y' = 0$ ($\varphi = 15°$ N), to $+\Gamma$ at $y' = \pi$ ($\varphi = 50°$ N). A unit distance equals 35° latitude/π, or 1032 km. In these units r' is the latitudinal width of the ocean basin, and $\gamma\xi$ the distance from the western boundary.

Two considerable simplifications result from working with the vertically integrated equations. In the first place, we can examine the case of a baroclinic ocean without having to specify the vertical distribution of density and current; secondly, only the vertical stresses at the upper boundaries need to be specified, and those can be computed from the known wind field over the ocean.

For a wind system we set

$$\tau_x = -\Gamma \cos ny, \quad \tau_y = 0 \tag{3}$$

giving maximum easterlies at $y = 0$ (latitude 15°) and maximum westerlies at $y = \pi/n$ (see fig. 1). The method can easily be extended to an arbitrary distribution of zonal winds, and under certain conditions to a general wind stress field (WOC).

Assume a triangular ocean basin with the dimensions shown in fig. 1. For the boundary conditions along AC and BC we choose

$$\psi_{\text{bdry}} = 0, \quad (\partial\psi/\partial\nu)_{\text{bdry}} = 0 \tag{4a, b}$$

where ν is normal to the boundary. Along AB

$$\psi_{\text{bdry}} = 0, \quad (\partial^2\psi/\partial\nu^2)_{\text{bdry}} = 0. \tag{5a, b}$$

Equations (4a) and (5a) state that the boundary ABCA is a stream line. According to (4b) no slippage takes place along the land boundary ACB, whereas according to (5b) no lateral shear exists along the sea boundary AB. The boundary conditions are equivalent to those imposed on a rigid plate clamped along the coast line ACB and supported along the latitude line AB (WOC).

Solution by boundary layer method

Introducing the non-dimensional parameters $\psi' = \beta\psi/\Gamma$, $r' = nr$, $x' = nx$, $y' = ny$, $n^4\nabla'^4 = \nabla^4$, and writing $k^3 \equiv \beta/A$, equation (1) becomes

$$\left(\gamma^3\nabla'^4 - \frac{\partial}{\partial x'}\right)\psi' = \sin y', \tag{6}$$

where $\gamma = n/k$ is the ratio of the wind wave-number n to the "Coriolis friction" wave-number k. The distance π/n between the easterlies and maximum westerlies is roughly 3500 km; it will be shown that

$$\frac{2\pi(\sec\Theta)^{4/3}}{\sqrt{3}\,k}$$

is roughly the latitudinal width of the western currents, say 350 km. Setting $\Theta = 60°$ for the Pacific gives $\gamma \approx .035$.

Inspection of equation (6) now shows that the problem belongs in the "boundary layer" category. The leading term (which contains higher order derivatives than all other terms) has a coefficient $\gamma^3 \ll 1$. The asymptotic solution of equation (6) (i.e., the solution which becomes more and more exact as $\gamma^3 \to 0$) can therefore be anticipated to give a good approximation to the exact flow except in the vicinity of the boundary intersections.

The conventional procedure for obtaining this solution is the following. We find a particular solution of equation (6) by neglecting the term containing γ^3. Such a solution is

$$\psi'^C = -x' \sin y' + d \sin y'. \tag{7}$$

In order to obtain the homogeneous boundary layer solutions which lead to the determination of d and the satisfaction of the boundary conditions, it is convenient to introduce the following coordinate system (fig. 1):

$$\xi = \frac{x'}{\gamma} - \frac{\zeta}{\gamma}\tan\Theta, \quad \zeta = y', \tag{8}$$

so that

$$\psi'^C = (-\gamma\xi - \zeta\tan\Theta + d)\sin\zeta \tag{9}$$

and

$$\frac{\partial}{\partial x'} = \frac{1}{\gamma}\frac{\partial}{\partial \xi}, \frac{\partial}{\partial y'} = -\frac{1}{\gamma}\Phi \tan\Theta \frac{\partial}{\partial \xi} + \frac{\partial}{\partial \zeta}. \quad (10)$$

In equation (10)

$$\Phi(\varphi) = 1 - \frac{\zeta}{\gamma}\frac{dy}{d\zeta} = 1 - \frac{1}{3}(\varphi - \varphi_0)\tan\varphi \quad (11)$$

is a correction involving the *second* derivative of the Coriolis parameter. Here φ_0 is the latitude at which $y = \zeta = 0$, about 15° N. The correction is small at low latitudes and amounts to 25 per cent at 50° latitude.

It is seen that variations in the y-direction involve ζ explicitly as well as implicitly through ξ. Since $\gamma \ll 1$, it follows that only the latter need be considered, so that

$$\nabla'^4 \approx \gamma^{-4} p^{-3} \frac{\partial^4}{\partial \xi^4} \quad (12)$$

where

$$p^{-3} = (1 + \Phi^2 \tan^2\Theta)^2. \quad (13)$$

With these substitutions the asymptotic form of the homogeneous equation becomes

$$\left(\frac{\partial^4}{\partial \xi^4} - p^3 \frac{\partial}{\partial \xi}\right)\psi' = 0 \quad (14)$$

with the solution $\psi' = \psi'^W + \psi'^E$, where

$$\psi'^W = \frac{1}{2}(a + ib)\, e^{-\frac{1}{2}(1+\sqrt{3}\,i)p\xi} \sin\zeta + \frac{1}{2}(a - ib)\, e^{-\frac{1}{2}(1-\sqrt{3}\,i)p\xi} \sin\zeta, \quad (15)$$

$$\psi'^E = c\, e^{-p(r'/\gamma - \xi)} \sin\zeta. \quad (16)$$

It is seen that ψ'^W decreases exponentially with distance from the western boundary and $\psi'^C + \psi'^W$ is therefore the western boundary solution; similiarly $\psi'^C + \psi'^E$ is the eastern boundary solution; whereas ψ'^C is the solution in the central portion of the ocean.

The boundary conditions (5) along AB are already satisfied. The constants a, b, c and d can be evaluated from the boundary conditions along ABCA. Along the western boundary $\xi = 0$, and equations (4 a, b) give

$$-\zeta \tan\Theta + d + a = 0, \quad 2\gamma/p + a - \sqrt{3}\,b = 0.$$

Along the eastern boundary $\xi = r'/\gamma$, where $r' = r_0'(1 - \zeta/\pi)$ is the (non-dimensional) latitudinal width of the ocean, and $r'_0 = (\tan\Theta + \tan\alpha)$ the width at $\zeta = 0$. The eastern boundary conditions give

$$-r' - \zeta\tan\Theta + d + c = 0, \quad -\gamma/p + c = 0.$$

The boundary conditions can be combined to yield

$$a = -r'(1-\varepsilon), \quad c = r'\varepsilon,$$
$$\sqrt{3}\,b = -r'(1 - 3\varepsilon), \quad d = r'(1-\varepsilon) + \zeta\tan\Theta, \quad (17)$$

where $\varepsilon = \gamma/pr'$ is a small quantity. The approximation involved in the non-homogeneous term (7) can now be estimated by performing the operation indicated in equation (6) on ψ'^C:

$$\left(\gamma^3 \Delta'^4 - \frac{\partial}{\partial x'}\right)\psi'^C = \sin y' \left[1 - \gamma^3(d - x')\right].$$

The exact solution requires that the right side equal $\sin y'$. Since $d - x' = r'(1-\varepsilon) - \gamma\xi$, or r' at most, the neglected term is less than $\gamma^3 r'$, that is less than 1 per cent.

The solution becomes

$$\psi' = r'\sin\zeta\left[-\frac{2}{\sqrt{3}}\left(1 - \frac{3}{2}\varepsilon\right)e^{-\frac{1}{2}p\xi}\cos\left(\frac{\sqrt{3}}{2}p\xi + \frac{\sqrt{3}}{2}\varepsilon - \frac{\pi}{6}\right) + 1 - \varepsilon\left(p\xi - e^{p\xi - 1/\varepsilon} - 1\right)\right]. \quad (18)$$

For north-south boundaries, $\Theta = 0$, $p = 1$, and the equation reduces to the rectangular case discussed in (WOC). The first term in the bracket gives the variation of ψ' with x near the western boundary, as shown in fig. 2. It indicates a series of exponentially "damped" boundary vortices, with a strong north-flowing current and countercurrent in the western vortex, both of latitudinal width $2\pi/\sqrt{3}$ pk. The principal effect of the inclined western coast line is to widen the western current (measured normal to the boundary) by the factor

$$p^{-1}\cos\Theta \approx (\sec\Theta)^{1/3}$$

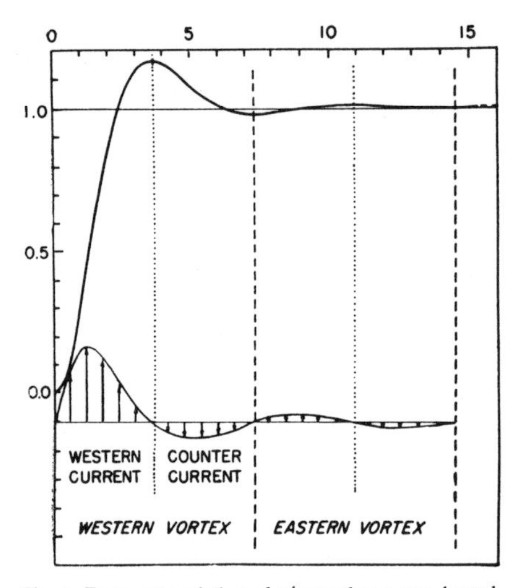

Fig. 2. East-west variation of ψ' near the western boundary for an infinitely wide ocean [equation (18) with $\varepsilon = 0$]. The arrows indicate the direction and intensity of the long-shore component of the current. Compare with Figures 4 to 6.

and to reduce the current intensity by a similar factor. The approximation refers to low latitudes; in high latitudes the modification associated with an inclination of the coast line is reduced, or even reversed. The total transport remains approximately the same. The inclination of the eastern boundary is important only insofar as it involves the width r of the oceans.

Circulation of the Pacific Ocean

Fig. 3 shows a chart of the Pacific Ocean on which north-south and west-east distances have been preserved. The basin north of 15° N is approximated by an isosceles triangle with a base of 13 units and altitude of 4 units (1 unit = 1032 km, see fig. 1). *A* rectangle is also drawn, which has the proper width at a latitude of 32.5° N midway between the easterly and westerly winds.

Figs. 4—6 show the computed stream lines in the triangular and rectangular ocean basins for the following numerical values of the parameters:

	Fig. 4	Fig. 5	Fig. 6
Shape of basin	triangle	rectangle	triangle
A in $cm^2 sec^{-1}$	$2.5 \cdot 10^7$	$2.5 \cdot 10^7$	10^8
π/n	35° lat.	35° lat.	35° lat.
At 30° N latitude:			
k in cm^{-1}	$2.0 \cdot 10^{-7}$	$2.0 \cdot 10^{-7}$	$1.25 \cdot 10^{-7}$
γ	.040	0.040	.064
p	.445	1.00	.445
$\frac{2\pi}{\sqrt{3pk}}$ in km	410	182	650
$\frac{2\pi}{\sqrt{3pk}} \cos \Theta$ in km	215	182	341

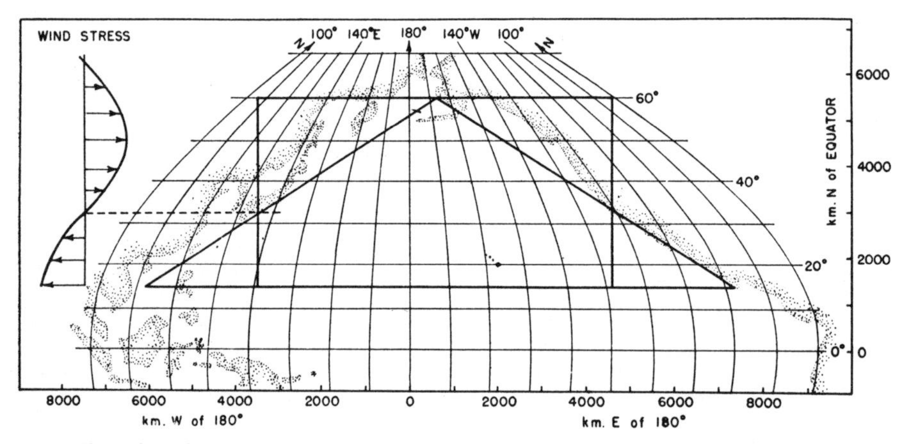

Fig. 3. Chart of Pacific Ocean. The outer scales give distances in km west or east of 180°, and north of equator. The circulation induced by a zonal wind stress distribution (shown to the left of the figure) has been computed for the cases of the triangular and rectangular oceans drawn in the figure.

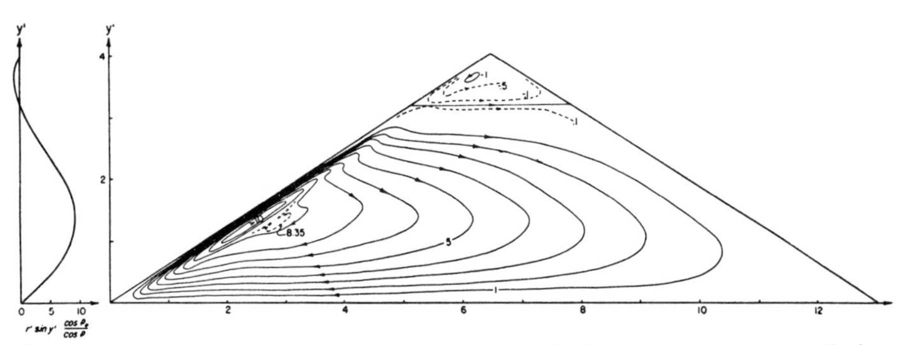

Fig. 4. Computed transport stream lines in the triangular ocean basin for $A = 2.5 \cdot 10^7$ cm² sec⁻¹. The lines represent equal values of $(\beta_0/\Gamma)\psi$. The curve to the left represents the variation of ψ with latitude. Unit distances along the x- and y-axis equal 1032 km. The section between $x = 1.5$ and $x = 4.0$, $y = 0.5$ and $y = 2.0$ has been redrawn on an enlarged scale in Figure 8.

The last two lines give the latitudinal and actual widths of the western current and countercurrent at the latitude 30°N where these currents attain their maximum intensity.

The stream lines are drawn[1] for equal values of

$$\frac{\beta_0}{\Gamma}\psi = \frac{\cos\varphi_0}{\cos\varphi}\, r' \sin\zeta\ [f(p\xi, \varepsilon)] \qquad (19)$$

where β_0 is the value of β at y' = 0. The function in the bracket is the one in equation (18). The expression preceding the bracket is a function of y only, and shown to the left of figs 4 and 5. In the case of the triangular ocean this function vanishes at latitudes 15° N, 50° N and 60° N, and accordingly divides the circulation into an anticyclonic and a cyclonic gyre. These gyres have been named the subtropical and subpolar gyres (WOC), and correspond roughly to the regions of the subtropical anticyclones and of the cyclonic storms, respectively. In the case of the rec-

[1] The approximations involved break down near the northern vertex of the triangle where the 2 boundary strips overlap. In this region the stream lines have been estimated. Because the real and abstracted boundaries differ greatly in this small region, it seems hardly worthwhile to devise special methods to compute the exact position of the theoretical stream lines.

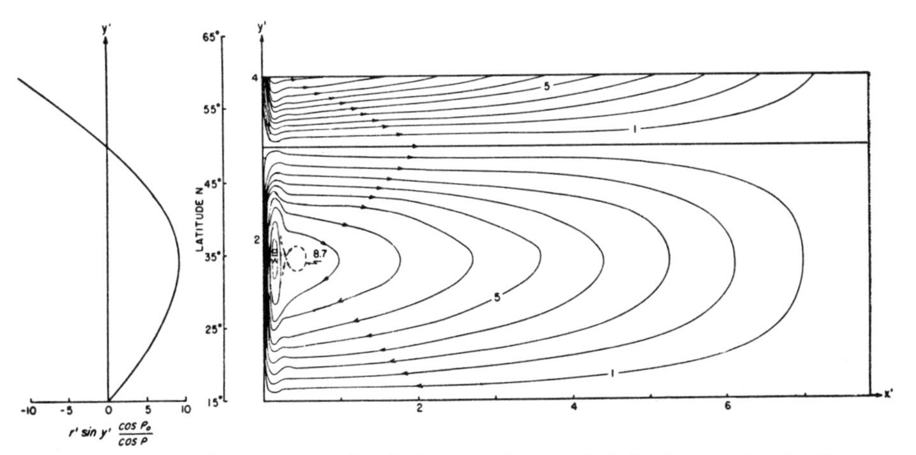

Fig. 5. Computed transport streamlines in the rectangular ocean basin for $A = 2.5 \cdot 10^7$ cm² sec⁻¹.

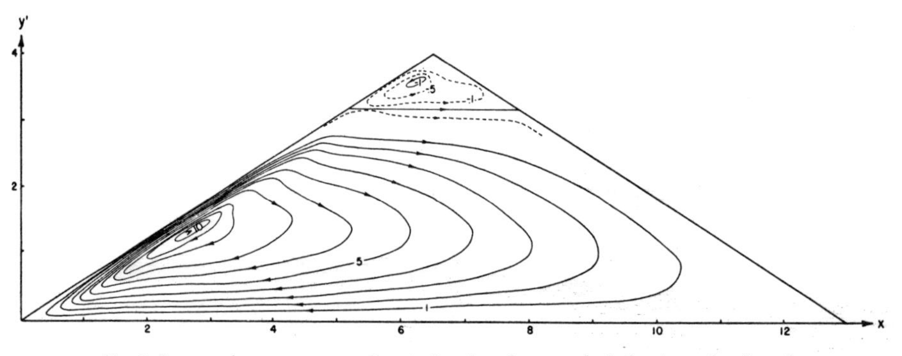

Fig. 6. Computed transport stream lines in the triangular ocean basin for $A = 10^8$ cm² sec⁻¹.

tangular ocean only part of the subpolar gyre is included.

The location and intensity of the gyres on figs. 4 and 6 compares favorably with oceanographic measurements, as presented in fig. 7. Note that the maximum transport of the western (Kuroshio) current takes place at 30° N latitude; that the ratio of mass transport of the Kuroshio Current to that of the Oyashio Current is of the order of 10:1. The eastern Pacific gyre and the California Current are the result of local meridional winds (WOC) and are therefore not present in our model for zonal winds.

Discrepancy between observed and computed transport

Computations based on the available wind data and the best available information concerning the relationship between wind speed at anemometer level and the stress exerted on the sea surface gives $\Gamma = 0.65$ dynes cm^{-2}. (WOC) Setting $\beta_0 = 2.2 \cdot 10^{-13}$ cm^{-1} sec^{-1} one finds that each unit of $\beta_0\, \psi/\Gamma$ as drawn on figs. 4—6 represents a transport of $3 \cdot 10^{12}$ *g* sec^{-1}, or 3 million metric tons sec^{-1}. This is one half the contour interval in fig. 7. We conclude that the computed *pattern* of water transport resembles the observed pattern quite closely, whereas the computed *quantity* of transport is about half the observed quantity.

This discrepancy cannot be ascribed to the value of the eddy viscosity, for, according to equation (18), the transport is almost independent of A. Nor can the discrepancy be ascribed to our assumption of no slippage against the western boundary. Taking the extreme case of *free slippage* against the western

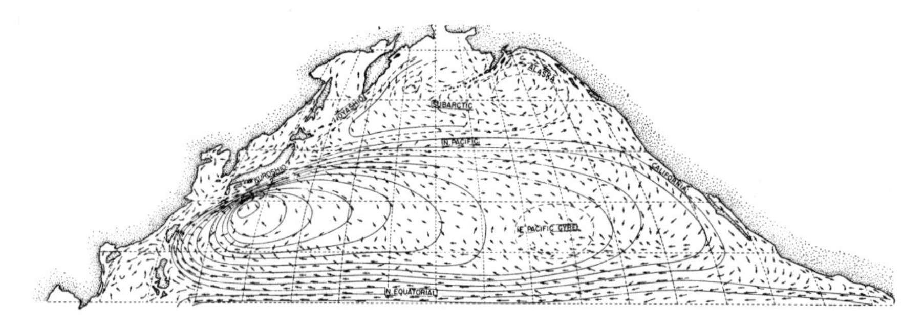

Fig. 7. Transport chart of the North Pacific as derived from oceanographic observations. Transport between adjacent stream lines are six million metric tons sec⁻¹. The stream lines are based on Fig. 205 of Sverdrup et al (1942), the arrows on the "Weltkarte zur Übersicht der Meereströmungen", Tafel 22, Deutsche Seewarte, *Ann. d. Hydrogr. u. Mar. Meteor.*, 1943. The projection is the same as the one in Figure 3.

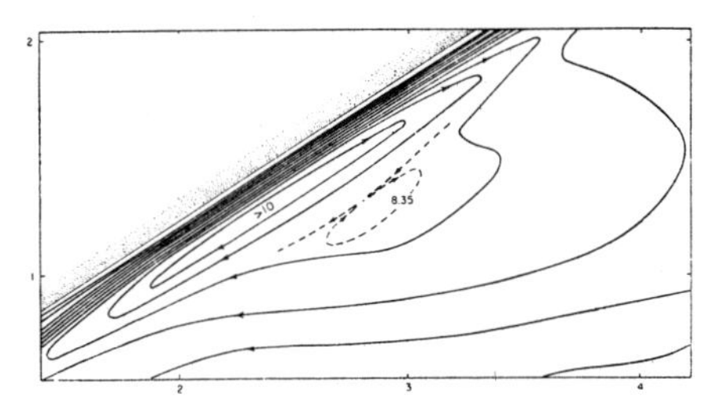

Fig. 8. Computed Pacific "Sargasso Sea" circulation in the triangular ocean basin for $A = 2.5 \cdot 10^7$ cm² sec⁻¹. This figure is an enlargement of the south-west portion of figure 4.

boundary by replacing boundary condition (4 b) with $\partial^2\psi/\partial v^2 = 0$ at $\xi = 0$, yields $b \approx + r'/\sqrt{3}$ (instead of $b \approx - r'/\sqrt{3}$), and

$$\psi'_{\max} = 1.30\ r' \sin \zeta \quad \text{at} \quad p\xi = 4\pi/3\sqrt{3}$$

instead of

$$\psi'_{\max} = 1.17\ r' \sin \zeta \quad \text{at} \quad p\xi = 2\pi/\sqrt{3}.$$

Thus with maximum velocity occurring directly against the boundary the western current has two-thirds its former width, and the transport is 20 per cent higher.

A more important modification may be related to the effect of the earth's rotation on lateral stress. Following the customary procedure we have, from analogy with the Navier-Stokes equations, introduced lateral stress into the integrated equations of motion through the term $A\nabla^2\mathbf{M}$. (WOC) Since the Navier-Stokes equations were derived for a resting coordinate system it would seem appropriate to replace the *relative* mass transport M by the absolute value $M + \mathbf{i}\,\Omega Rh \cos\varphi$, where $\mathbf{i}$ is the unit vector pointing eastward, and h the effective depth of the current. Performing the curl operation[1] one obtains an additional term

$$A\frac{\partial^3}{\partial y^3}(\Omega Rh \cos\varphi) = \frac{A\Omega h}{R^2}\sin\varphi$$

to be added to the wind curl on the right side of equation (1). Setting $A = 2.5 \cdot 10^7$ cm² sec⁻¹, $\varphi = 30°$, $h = 10^5$ cm, gives $2 \cdot 10^{-9} g$ sec⁻² compared to a wind curl of about $9 \cdot 10^{-9} g$ sec⁻². The effect would be to strengthen the transport in the subtropical gyre by about 25 per cent, to weaken the transport in the subpolar gyre, and to displace the boundary between the gyres northward.

[1] Here again we employ a plane coordinate system. In spherical coordinates the modification is several times larger. We hope to return to this problem in greater detail when considering a basin on a spherical earth.

The physical basis of this modification forms the substance of ROSSBY's (1936) discussion concerning the merits of Taylor's vorticity-transport theory and Prandtl's momentum-transport theory. If angular momentum is to be conserved, then any meridional interchange of eddies must induce a relative current setting eastward at high latitudes, and westward at low latitudes.

The discrepancy may also be ascribed to an underestimate of the surface stress for a given wind speed, especially at wind speeds of Beaufort four or less (WOC).

These remarks apply particularly to the western currents. In the case of the north equatorial current (of which only half is shown on figs. 4—6), the equatorial countercurrent, and the south equatorial current, SVERDRUP (1947) and REID (1948) have obtained satisfactory agreement between the transport computed from the wind stress and that computed from oceanographic observations.

The western boundary vortices (Sargasso Sea) and the value of *A*

An interesting feature is the double vortex system near the western boundary on figs. 4 and 5, which is shown on an enlarged scale on fig. 8. In the case of fig. 6 the small eastern vortex is absent, but its effect can still be noticed by the bulging of the stream lines.

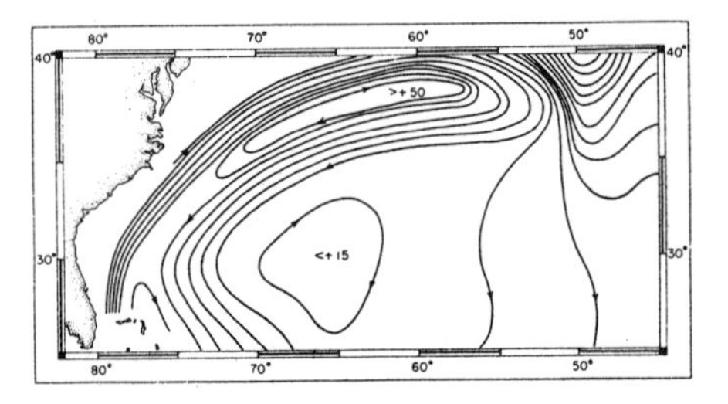

Fig. 9. Idealized topography of the sea level of the North Atlantic Ocean according to DEFANT (1941). The units are dynamic centimeters.

Whether the eastern vortex will or will not be present depends only on the width of the ocean and the value of the eddy viscosity, as will be seen from an inspection of equation (18). The curve in Fig. 2 represents a graph of the function $f(p\xi)$ in the bracket of equation (18) for an infinitely wide ocean ($\varepsilon = 0$). The function oscillates about the value of 1, and, strictly speaking, the vortex system extends to infinity, though the amplitudes of the vortices die off exponentially with distance from the western boundary. In the case of an ocean of (non-dimensional) width r' the function oscillates not about the horizontal line $f(p\,\xi) = 1$, but about the line $f(p\xi) = 1 - \varepsilon p\xi$. The eastern vortex exists only if the slope of the first term in the bracket of equation (18) at the distance $(p\xi)_m = 14\pi/\sqrt{3} = 8.45$, where it reaches its third maximum, exceeds the slope $-\varepsilon$ of the asymptotic line; that is, if

$$\varepsilon < \frac{2}{\sqrt{3}} e^{-\frac{1}{2}(p\xi)_m} \sin\left[\frac{\sqrt{3}}{2}(p\xi)_m\right] = 0.015.$$

The corresponding conditions on γ and A are:

$$\gamma < 0.015\,pr',\ A < \frac{(0.015\,pr')^3\,\beta}{n^3}.$$

For the Pacific at latitude 30° N, $p = .445$, $r' = 8.6$, $\beta = 2 \cdot 10^{-13}$ cm^{-1} sec^{-1}, $\pi/n = 3\,900$ km, which gives $A < 8.25 \cdot 10^7$ cm^2 sec^{-1}. For the Atlantic at the same latitude, $\Theta \approx 50°$, $p = .625$, $r' = 6.0$, and $A < 7.8 \cdot 10^7$ cm^{2}sec^{-1} in order for the eastern vortex to exist.

In terms of the dynamic topography of the sea surface the double vortex system represents two humps in the sea surface, the western hump being much larger than the eastern hump (fig. 8). The two humps are separated by a trough running parallel to the western current with a saddle point directly between the humps. Observations in the Pacific Ocean are inconclusive with respect to the existence of the eastern hump. The corresponding area in the Atlantic, the Sargasso Sea, is one of the most intensely studied areas in the world, but even so the conclusions are uncertain. DEFANT's (1941) analysis of the dynamic topography based on observations from the *Meteor* expedition, and previous expeditions, is reproduced in fig. 9. It shows a small hump in the Bermuda area, but according to Defant (personal communication) the data was not quite convincing in this respect. At Defant's suggestion FELBER (1934) had previously analyzed the extensive observational material based on surface drifts of vessels, and his stream lines show a saddle point southwest of Bermuda throughout the year. His figure for April is reproduced in fig. 10.

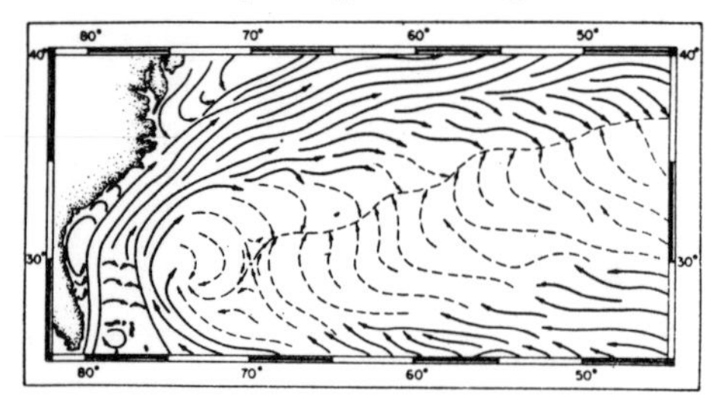

Fig. 10. Stream lines in the north-west Atlantic from the surface drift of ships, according to Felber (1934).

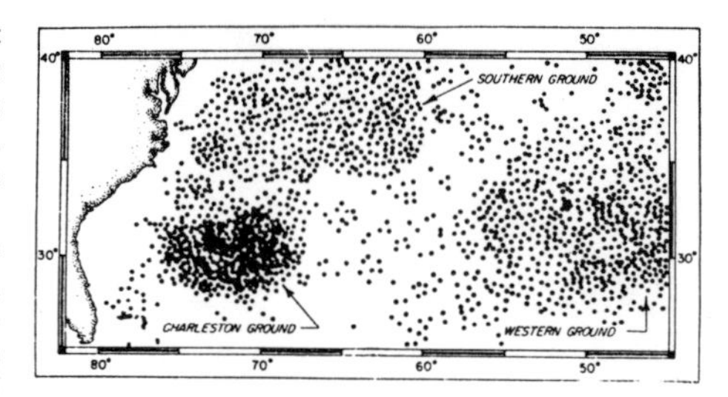

Fig. 11. Distribution of the sperm whale based on log-book records dating from 1761—1920 (according to TOWNSEND 1935). Each point represents the position of a whale ship on a day when one or more whales were taken.

Defant's and Felber's analyses are consistent with respect to the existence of a saddle point at about 70° west, 30° north, but they differ regarding the Gulf Stream countercurrent. This discrepancy has to do with the different methods of averaging employed by the two authors. The large number of observations[1] collected since Defant summarized the data in 1941 have made increasingly clear the variability of the circulation in the Bermuda area,

[1] We are indebted to C. O'D. Iselin, F. Fuglister, and A. Worthington of the Woods Hole Oceanographic Institute for having made these observations available to us.

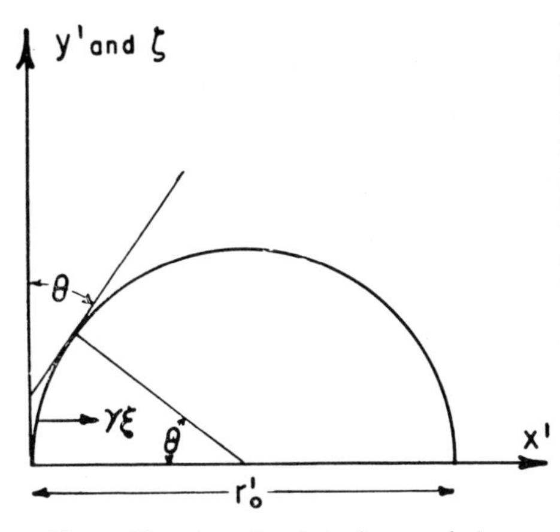

Fig. 12. Dimensions of semi-circular ocean basin.

and the shifting in position from season to season, even from week to week, of the Gulf Stream and related features (ISELIN and FUGLISTER, 1948). Defant's analysis is based on synoptic profiles, each of which reveals a countercurrent seaward of the Gulf Stream, occurring however at different locations for different cruises. Felber's averaging at fixed geographic location would naturally tend to obscure secondary features adjacent to strong but wandering primary features. The differences are somewhat similar to the differences between synoptic weather maps and climatic charts.

No suitable methods have yet been developed for combining results from different cruises to bring out the existence of secondary features such as the countercurrent and the eastern vortex. For this reason observations collected since 1941 have not added materially to our understanding of the Sargasso Sea circulation, but most of these observations indicate a north-flowing current west of Bermuda. A curious clustering in the distribution of sperm whales may perhaps be interpreted as evidence for the existence of the two vortices and the trough. Each point in fig. 11 represents the position of a whale ship on a day when one or more whales were taken, according to logbook records dating from 1761 to 1920 (TOWNSEND, 1935). Relatively few points are found in the region of the trough, yet there appear to have been no reasons for whaling ships to avoid this region. These troughs, according to Felber's presentation, are regions of convergence. In such regions the concentration of nutrients is small, and one may expect a relatively small concentration of plankton, and of sperm whales which feed on plankton. It is not impossible that the two vortices represent optimum conditions for the existence of plankton, these being the areas where freely floating organisms would remain for the longest time under uniform environmental conditions.

In a comparison of figs. 5—8 one must keep in mind that fig. 8 applies to the Pacific Ocean, whereas figs. 5—7 apply to the Atlantic. As a whole, the evidence, though far from conclusive, seems to support the existence of the eastern vortex, and would therefore indicate that the lateral eddy viscosity in this region is less than $7.8 \cdot 10^7$ cm² sec⁻¹.

The effect of curvature in the boundaries

It has been stated previously that the present method can be extended to an ocean basin of arbitrary shape provided the boundaries are not too irregular. To express this in quantitative form, consider a semi-circular basin of diameter (not radius) r'_0 (fig. 12). For a coordinate system we choose

$$\xi = \frac{x'}{\gamma} - \frac{r'_0}{2\gamma}(1 - \cos\Theta), \quad \zeta = \frac{r'_0}{2}\sin\Theta,$$

where, as previously, $\gamma\xi$ is the non-dimensional distance from the western boundary, Θ its inclination relative to a north-south direction, and r'_0 is the width of the basin at $y' = 0$. Differentiation leads to the same transformation as given by (10) except that Θ now depends on ζ. Neglecting variations in γ, we obtain

$$\nabla^2 = \frac{1}{\gamma^3}\left(\sec^2\Theta\frac{\partial^2}{\partial\xi^2} - \frac{2\gamma}{r'_0}\sec^3\Theta\frac{\partial^2}{\partial\xi\partial\zeta} + \dots\right)$$

The second term is a correction for the curvature of the coastline. This correction is small provided the radius of curvature

$$\frac{1}{2}r'_0 \gg \gamma\sec\Theta.$$

As an extreme example of irregular boundaries consider the sharp change in the orientation of the eastern seaboard between Jacksonville, Florida, and Savannah, Georgia. Setting $\Theta = 0.04$ would require the radius of curvature to be large compared to .04 units of distance, or 40 km. The actual radius of curvature is 160 km.

Conclusions

The present method appears to be suitable for a numerical computation of the gross features in the ocean circulation, taking into account the outlines of the actual boundaries. The simple models discussed here give an indication of the results of such a computation. Changes in the orientation of the coast line will lead to a widening or narrowing of the western current, but the general features should be more or less the same, irrespective of the boundaries. This is in agreement with the fact that the general circulation is similar in the various oceans, whereas the ocean boundaries are not.

Acknowledgement

We are indebted to Mr P. Osborn for his assistance in preparing the figures.

REFERENCES

DEFANT, A., 1941: Die absolute Topographie des physikalischen Meeresniveaus und der Druckflächen, sowie die Wasserbewegungen im Atlantischen Ozean. *Deutsche Atlantische Exped. Meteor 1925—1927, Wiss. Erg.*, Bd **6**, 2 Teil, 5 Lief., fig. 41.

FELBER, O.-H., 1934: Oberflächenströmungen des Nordatlantischen Ozeans zwischen 15° and 50° n. B. *Arch. d. Deutschen Seewarte*, **53**, 1, pp. 5—17.

HIDAKA, K., 1949: Mass transport in ocean currents and the Lateral Mixing. *Geoph. Notes*, Tokyo Univ., **2**, 3, pp. 1—4.

ISELIN, C. O'D., and FUGLISTER, F. C., 1948: Some Recent Developments in the study of the Gulf Stream. *Journ. of Marine Res.*, **7**, (Sverdrup Anniv. Vol.) pp. 317—329.

MUNK, W. H., 1950: On the Wind-driven Ocean Circulation. *Journ. of Met.*, **7**, pp. 79—93.

REID, R. O., 1948: The Equatorial Currents of the Eastern Pacific as Maintained by the Stress of the Wind. *Journ. of Marine Res.*, **7**, pp. 74—99.

ROSSBY, C.-G., 1936: Dynamics of Steady Ocean Currents in the Light of Experimental Fluid Mechanics. *Pap. Phys. Oceanogr. and Met.*, **5**, 1, 43 pp.

SVERDRUP, H. U. and collaborators, 1942: The Oceans, Their Physics, Chemistry, and General Biology. Prentice-Hall, New York, 1087 pp.

SVERDRUP, H. U., 1947: Wind-driven currents in a baroclinic ocean; with Application to the Equatorial Currents of the Eastern Pacific. *Proc. Nat. Acad. Sci.*, **33**, pp. 318—326.

TOWNSEND, C. H., 1935: The Distribution of Certain Whales as Shown by Logbook Records of American Whale Ships. *Zoologic*, **19**, 1, pp. 2—50.

Steady flow in a frictionless homogeneous ocean

N. P. Fofonoff

Reprinted with permission from Sears Foundation: Journal of Marine Research Volume 13, Number 3, pages 254 through 262, 1954

STEADY FLOW IN A FRICTIONLESS HOMOGENEOUS OCEAN[1]

BY

N. P. FOFONOFF[2]

Brown University, Providence 12, R. I.

ABSTRACT

A mathematical model is developed to study the free (frictionless) steady horizontal flow which can occur in a homogeneous ocean of constant depth. The flow satisfies the dynamic constraint that the vertical component of absolute vorticity is constant along a streamline. The conclusion is reached that in an enclosed ocean a free steady circulation cannot have any slow broad eastward currents. The eastward currents must occur as narrow streams of high velocity and high relative vorticity. Intensified currents are present along the eastern and western coasts.

The theory which is developed for the homogeneous ocean of constant depth can be applied to the two-layer ocean if the horizontal divergence of flow is negligible. If the horizontal divergence is not negligible, then the intensification of poleward currents is more pronounced and that of equatorward currents less pronounced as compared with the homogeneous ocean.

INTRODUCTION

The theoretical models of the wind-induced oceanic circulation developed by Stommel (1948), Munk (1950), and others have contributed a great deal to the understanding of some large-scale features of the circulation in the major oceans, but these models are limited by the fact that they are based on linearized equations and on the artificial concept of eddy viscosity. It is possible that significant features of oceanic circulation cannot be simulated by a model in which the nonlinear terms, i. e., the relative-acceleration terms, are neglected. Attempts to improve and extend these models are hindered by the analytical complexity of a model which includes both relative accelerations and dissipative effects.

In the present paper, simple types of ideal fluid motion are studied in order to describe characteristic features of steady free circulation in an enclosed ocean. By considering an ideal fluid, the analytical difficulties presented by the nonlinear terms in the hydrodynamic equations

[1] Technical Report 8, Office of Naval Research contract N7onr-358(11), NR 083-050 with Brown University. Paper presented 5 May 1954 at American Geophysical Union annual meeting, Washington, D. C.

[2] Now with Pacific Oceanographic Group, Nanaimo, B. C.

are avoided. It is possible to show that some features of oceanic circulation, e.g., the westward intensification of the circulation, exist in the absence of friction.

The simplest model that includes accelerations in the flow is a frictionless homogeneous constant-depth ocean in which the water moves horizontally in the absence of driving forces. This model does not contain any mechanism by which free flow can be established from a state of rest, but it does contain certain dynamic restrictions which must be satisfied by an existing free flow. For steady flow, the most important constraint is that the vertical component of absolute vorticity is constant along a streamline. This constraint on the absolute vorticity is stringent, because the change of the Coriolis parameter over a few degrees of latitude is, over most of the real ocean, about two orders of magnitude greater than the relative vorticity of the flow. It is apparent, therefore, that the possible types of free flow are severely restricted in the ocean.

Rossby (1936) has considered the dynamic constraint on the vertical component of absolute vorticity in his study of the Gulf Stream, but his analysis did not extend to the entire ocean. In the study of free atmospheric flow, there has been more progress and some attempts have been made to adapt the results of these studies to circulation in the oceans. Høiland (1950) found particular examples of free flow which he applied to the ocean. Although these examples agree qualitatively with the free flows discussed in the present paper, Høiland fails to point out the pronounced characteristics that the free flow would exhibit.

ASSUMPTIONS AND NOTATION

The ocean model chosen in this analysis consists of a homogeneous body of water of constant depth bounded by smooth vertical lateral boundaries. The motion is assumed to be horizontal and uniform with depth. The effects of thermohaline structure, compressibility, and frictional forces are neglected everywhere. Vertical motions and accelerations are also neglected so that the pressure is simply determined by the hydrostatic equation.

The unit vector $\mathbf{k}$ is directed vertically upward, and z is the vertical distance measured upward from a level undisturbed ocean surface. The ocean surface in the model is at $z = \eta$. The horizontal velocity is designated by $\mathbf{v}$ and the stream function of the horizontal circulation by ψ. The vertical component of absolute vorticity ζ_a equals $f + \zeta$, where f is the Coriolis parameter and ζ is the vertical component of relative vorticity. The quantity Q is introduced for $p/\rho + \frac{1}{2}(\mathbf{v}\cdot\mathbf{v}) + gz$, where p is pressure, ρ density, and g acceleration of gravity.

EQUATIONS OF MOTION

The equations of motion, consistent with the assumptions made above, may be written

$$(\mathbf{v}\cdot\nabla)\,\mathbf{v} + f(\mathbf{k}\times\mathbf{v}) = -\nabla p/\rho\,, \tag{1}$$

$$\nabla\cdot\mathbf{v} = 0\,, \tag{2}$$

$$p = \rho g(\eta - z)\,, \tag{3}$$

where the differential vector operator ∇ refers to the horizontal coordinates only.

Equation (1) may be written $\zeta_a(\mathbf{k}\times\mathbf{v}) = -\nabla Q$ or

$$\zeta_a\mathbf{v} = -\nabla\times(Q\mathbf{k})\,, \tag{4}$$

where

$$Q = g\eta + \tfrac{1}{2}(\mathbf{v}\cdot\mathbf{v})\,. \tag{5}$$

The velocity stream function ψ is defined by the equation

$$\mathbf{v} = \nabla\times(\psi\mathbf{k})\,. \tag{6}$$

Elimination of $\mathbf{v}$ from equation (4) yields

$$\zeta_a\nabla\psi = -\nabla Q\,, \tag{7}$$

so that

$$Q = Q(\psi)\,, \tag{8}$$

$$\zeta_a = -dQ/d\psi\,. \tag{9}$$

Equation (9) is a statement of the well known result that the vertical component of absolute vorticity is constant along a streamline. This equation expresses the basic dynamic constraint to be satisfied by the steady free motion in a homogeneous ocean.

DIMENSIONAL ANALYSIS

The following dimensional constants are chosen as being representative of a typical ocean:

L_0 = 2000 km, a typical horizontal length;
f_0 = 10^{-4}, a typical value of the Coriolis parameter,
η_0 = 100 cm, a typical displacement of the free surface from the undisturbed level $z = 0$;
g = 10^3 cm sec^{-2}, gravity.

The equations are converted into nondimensional form by introducing the nondimensional variables $\mathbf{v}' = \mathbf{v}/U$, where U is a characteristic velocity, $\psi' = \psi/UL_0$, $Q' = Q/g_0$, $\zeta_a' = \zeta_a/f_0$, $f' = f/f'_0$, $\zeta' = \zeta/(U/L_0)$, and $\nabla' = L_0\nabla$, the nondimensional differential operator.

By choosing $U = g\eta_0/f_0L_0 = 5$ cm sec^{-1} and defining $\delta = U/f_0L_0 = 2.5 \times 10^{-4}$, the nondimensional form of (6), (8), and (9) may be written

$$\mathbf{v}' = \nabla' \times (\psi'\mathbf{k}) \, , \tag{10}$$

$$Q' = Q'(\psi') = \eta' + \tfrac{1}{2}\, \delta(\mathbf{v}' \cdot \mathbf{v}') \, , \tag{11}$$

$$\zeta_a' = - \, dQ'/d\psi' = f' + \delta\zeta' = f' - \delta\nabla'^2\psi' \, . \tag{12}$$

THE VORTICITY EQUATION

The vorticity equation (12) contains two unknown functions, ψ' and ζ_a', whereas (11) contains three unknown functions, ψ', Q', and η'. Therefore the motion is restricted only by (12), because η' can always be chosen to satisfy (11) once ψ' and ζ_a' are determined. Equation (12) does not determine the motion uniquely, because the vertical component of absolute vorticity can be any function of the stream function.

It is evident from (12) that, unless relative vorticities comparable with the Coriolis parameter (i.e., $\zeta' \sim 1/\delta$) are present in the flow, the stream function will be a function of f' only and the flow will be along latitude circles only. It follows, therefore, that in the vicinity of meridional boundaries where the flow must be across latitude circles, the relative vorticity and hence the velocity must be much larger than the average for the ocean. It is not possible to have in an enclosed ocean a steady free circulation which does not contain relatively large velocities unless the circulation is confined to a narrow range of latitude. For certain choices of $\zeta_a'(\psi')$, the circulation cannot be slow, e.g., $\zeta_a' =$ constant. In order to obtain a steady free circulation that is slow over most of the ocean, restrictions must be imposed upon the choice of $\zeta_a'(\psi')$. The nature of these restrictions is illustrated by considering a simple example.

A SIMPLE EXAMPLE OF FREE FLOW

A rectangular nondimensional coordinate system x', y' is introduced with the positive x'-axis eastward and the positive y'-axis northward. A rectangular region with sides a', b' is chosen to represent the ocean. The function $\zeta_a'(\psi')$ is assumed to be a linear function of ψ', so that (12) becomes

$$f' - \delta\nabla'^2\psi' = c_0 + c_1\psi' \, , \tag{13}$$

where c_0 and c_1 are constants.

The boundary condition on ψ' is that the ocean boundary is a streamline. This condition is satisfied by requiring the stream function to be zero along the ocean boundary.

The Coriolis parameter is assumed to be a linear function of y' of the form $f' = f_0' + \beta y'$.

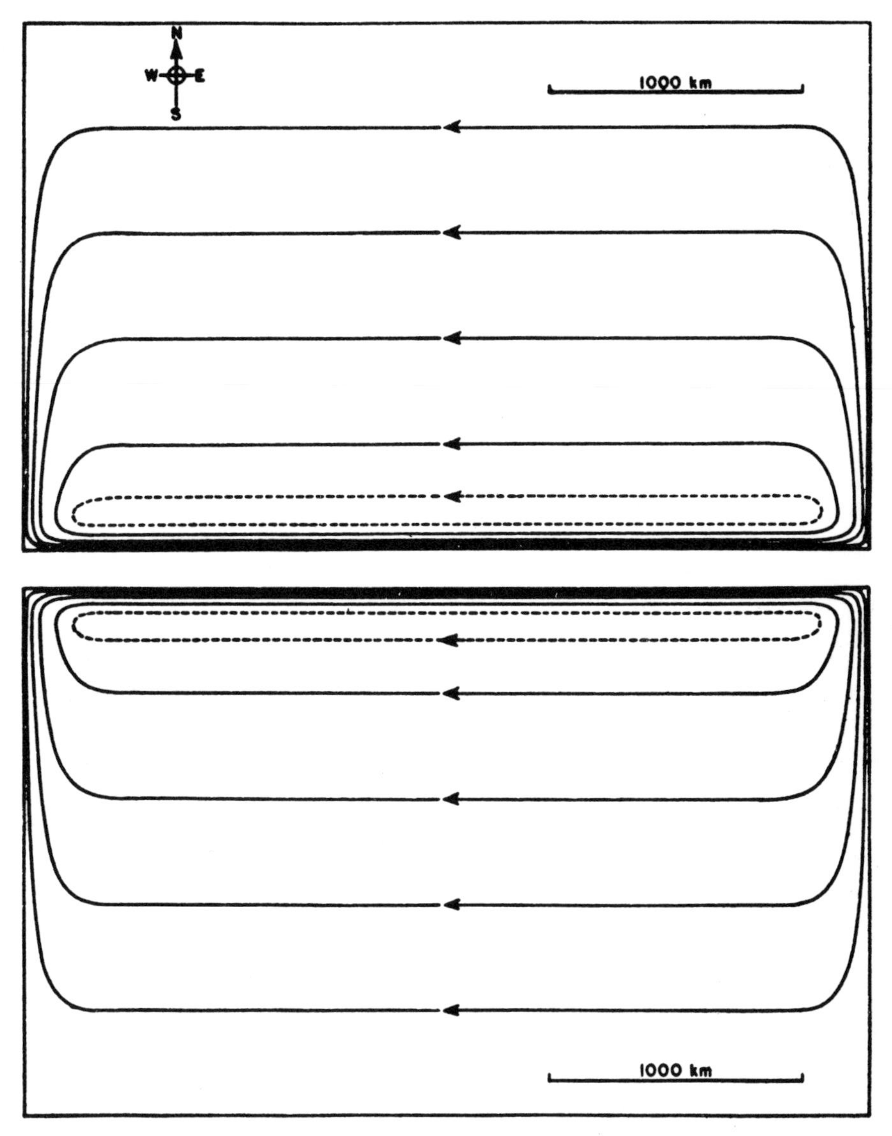

Figure 1. Streamlines of free flow in a homogeneous ocean, computed from equation (15) for $y_0' = b'$, $b' = 1$ in the upper diagram and for $y_0' = 0$, $b' = 1$ in the lower diagram. The number b' is the ratio of the meridional extent of the ocean to L_0.

By defining u_0' and y_0' so that $u_0' = \beta/c_1$ and $y_0' = (c_0 - f_0')/c_1$, equation (13) may be written

$$(u_0'\delta/\beta)\nabla'^2\psi' + \psi' = u_0'(y' - y_0') . \tag{14}$$

In equation (14), u_0' is a nondimensional velocity, δ a ratio of relative vorticity to the Coriolis parameter, and β the nondimensional northward variation of the Coriolis parameter.

Wherever the relative vorticity is negligible, the velocity is given by u_0'; eastward if u_0' is positive and westward if negative. A study of (14) reveals (a) that the relative vorticity in an enclosed ocean can be negligible only if u_0' is negative and (b) that all eastward currents

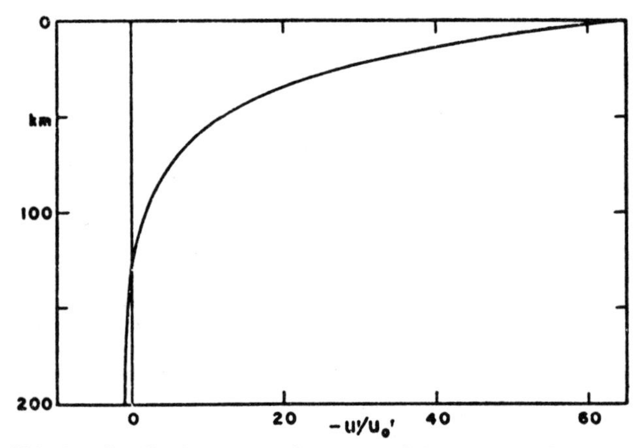

Figure 2. Velocity distribution across the eastward jet, computed for $y_0' = 0$, $b' = 1$, and $L_0 = 2000$ km. The number b' is the ratio of the meridional extent of the ocean to L_0.

must occur as narrow streams of high velocity and high relative vorticity.

Although the exact solution of (14) can be obtained, the simpler approximate solution obtained by boundary-layer methods is more convenient. The boundary-layer solution may be written

$$\psi' = u_0'\{(y' - y_0') + y_0'\exp(-y'/\varepsilon) - (b' - y_0')\exp[-(b' - y')/\varepsilon]\} \times \{1 - \exp(-x'/\varepsilon) - \exp[-(a' - x')/\varepsilon]\} , \tag{15}$$

where $\varepsilon = (|u_0'\delta/\beta|)^{\frac{1}{2}}$. This solution is valid so long as $b'/\varepsilon \gg 1$ and $a'/\varepsilon \gg 1$.

In Fig. 1, streamlines of the free flow are shown for $y_0' = b'$, $b' = 1$ in the upper diagram and for $y_0' = 0$, $b' = 1$ in the lower diagram. These diagrams may be joined to give a symmetrical jet along the middle of the ocean, flanked by broad westward currents to the north and south. The velocity distribution across the eastward jet for $y_0' = 0$, $b' = 1$ is computed from the equation

$$u'/u_0' = 1 - (1/\varepsilon) \exp[-(1 - y')/\varepsilon]$$

and is shown in Fig. 2. All the figures are based on computations for which $\varepsilon^2 = 2.5 \times 10^{-4}$.

DISCUSSION

It is apparent from the preceding analysis that the free steady circulation in an enclosed ocean has distinctive features due to the variation of Coriolis parameter with latitude. The circulation, characterized by a slow westward drift over the major portion of the ocean, is accelerated and concentrated into a swift current along the western boundary of the ocean. The eastward current occurs as a narrow stream of high velocity and high relative vorticity. This eastward jet which crosses the ocean at constant speed is decelerated and spread out along the eastern boundary of the ocean. A slow, broad, eastward current cannot exist in the steady state.

The east-west symmetry of the stream function for the homogeneous ocean cannot exist if any dissipation is present. The swift current along the eastern boundary of the ocean, which must be supplied by a jet, is very sensitive to losses of relative vorticity in the jet.

The concentration of the westward drift into an eastward jet would occur in the real ocean if frictional stresses were insufficient to decelerate the current along the western boundary of the ocean. The presence of the Gulf Stream in the open ocean northeast of Cape Hatteras suggests that a considerable portion of the momentum and relative vorticity of the Stream actually reaches the open ocean and is dissipated there.

EXTENSION TO THE TWO-LAYER OCEAN

Most of the real ocean has a more or less clearly defined upper layer which contains the relatively strong motion and which represents the portion of the ocean influenced by wind stress. Below this layer there is a much larger body of water of greater density which shows little motion and little response to the prevailing atmospheric state. This picture of the ocean has often been represented in theoretical considerations, in idealized form, by the two-layer ocean consisting of two homogeneous layers of water of different densities with the motion confined entirely to the upper less dense layer.

The two-layer ocean in its undisturbed state may be completely specified by giving the lateral boundaries, the densities ρ_0 and ρ_1 of the upper and lower layers respectively, and the volume V_0 of the upper layer. In order to adapt the analysis of the homogeneous ocean to the two-layer ocean, the additional quantities η_1, h, ψ, σ, γ are introduced and defined as follows: $z = \eta_1$, the equation for the interface between the two layers; $h = \eta + \eta_1$, the thickness of the upper layer; ψ, the stream function of volume transport; $\sigma = \nabla \cdot \mathbf{v}$, the divergence of the horizontal velocity; $\gamma = \rho_0/(\rho_1 - \rho_0)$.

The pressure in the lower layer is given by

$$p = \rho_0 g(\eta + \eta_1) - \rho_1 g(z + \eta_1) . \tag{16}$$

The condition for no motion in the lower layer requires the horizontal pressure gradient to be zero everywhere in the lower layer, so that

$$\begin{aligned} \nabla\eta_1 &= \gamma\nabla\eta , \\ \eta_1 &= \gamma\eta + h_0 , \\ h &= (1 + \gamma)\eta + h_0 . \end{aligned} \tag{17}$$

The arbitrary constant h_0 is determined from the specified volume V_0 of the upper layer, or from an equivalent condition.

The equations for the two-layer ocean, analogous to equations (5), (6), and (9) for the homogeneous ocean, are

$$\mathbf{v}h = \nabla \times (\psi\mathbf{k}) , \tag{18}$$

$$Q = Q(\psi) = g(h - h_0)/(1 + \gamma) + \tfrac{1}{2}(\mathbf{v}\cdot\mathbf{v}) , \tag{19}$$

$$\zeta_a'/h = - dQ/d\psi . \tag{20}$$

The corresponding nondimensional equations for the two-layer ocean are formed by introducing the additional nondimensional variables h', ψ', σ', defined as $h' = h/h_0$, $\psi' = \psi/Uh_0L_0$, $\sigma' = \sigma/(U/L_0)$, and the nondimesnional parameter α, defined as $\alpha = (1 + \gamma)\eta_0/h_0$.

The nondimensional equations which form the dynamic constraints for free motion in the two-layer ocean are

$$\zeta_a'/h' = - dQ'/d\psi' , \tag{21}$$

$$Q'(\psi') = (1/\alpha)(h' - 1) + \tfrac{1}{2}\delta(\mathbf{v}'\cdot\mathbf{v}') , \tag{22}$$

where $\zeta_a' = f' + \delta\zeta'$ and $h' = 1 + \alpha\eta'$.

Equations (21) and (22) contain three unknown functions each and must be solved simultaneously. Thus, in the two-layer ocean, (22) is restrictive in contrast with (11) which is not restrictive. As in the homogeneous ocean, the circulation is not uniquely determined, because ζ_a'/h' can be any function of ψ'.

No solutions of the equations for the two-layer ocean have been obtained. The circulation in the upper layer will resemble the circulation in the homogeneous ocean if the divergence σ' can be neglected.

The divergence is small if the change in thickness of the upper layer along a streamline is small compared with the total thickness of the upper layer, i.e., if α is small compared with unity.

In high-velocity regions of the two-layer ocean the thickness of the upper layer is reduced, so that the absolute vorticity is smaller in magnitude than the absolute vorticity in a corresponding region of the homogeneous ocean. For a two-layer ocean located in the northern hemisphere, the relative vorticity must be less than the relative vorticity in the homogeneous ocean for corresponding flows. Therefore, the intensification of a current flowing toward the pole is more pronounced and that of a current flowing toward the equator is less pronounced than the intensification of a corresponding current in the homogeneous ocean.

REFERENCES

HØILAND, E.
1950. On horizontal motion in a rotating fluid. Geofys. Publ., *17*(10): 5–26.
MUNK, W. H.
1950. On the wind-driven ocean circulation. J. Meteorol., *7*(2): 79–93.
ROSSBY, C.-G.
1936. Dynamics of steady ocean currents in the light of experimental fluid mechanics. Pap. phys. Oceanogr. Meteorol., *5*(1): 1–43.
STOMMEL, HENRY
1948. The westward intensification of wind-driven ocean currents. Trans. Amer. geophys. Un., *29*(2): 202–206.

The Gulf Stream as an inertial boundary layer

J. G. Charney

Reprinted with permission from Proceedings of the National Academy of Sciences
Volume 41, Number 10,
pages 731 through 740, 1955

THE GULF STREAM AS AN INERTIAL BOUNDARY LAYER

By J. G. Charney

INSTITUTE FOR ADVANCED STUDY*

Communicated June 8, 1955

Introduction.—Notable advances have been made in our understanding of the ocean circulations in the past few years. The general westward intensification of the wind-driven circulation was shown by Stommel[1] to be a consequence of the variation of the vertical component of the earth's angular velocity. Owing to a tendency toward conservation of absolute vertical vorticity, a fluid column moving poleward in the Northern Hemisphere acquires a relative clockwise spin, and a fluid column moving Equatorward a counterclockwise spin. As a result, the clockwise circulation of the ocean is intensified in the west and reduced in the east. Using actual wind stresses, Munk[2] was able to account for the principal features of the mean circulation of the open ocean. The detailed structure of the western current remained, however, essentially unexplained. The eddy-frictional mechanism employed by Munk to provide the necessary energy dissipation for the entire ocean was inapplicable to the individual boundary current. In order to account for the observed width of the current, Munk was forced to postulate an eddy viscosity so large that the eddy sizes were themselves comparable to the width. Such eddies are observed in the meanderings of the boundary current after it leaves the continental slope but are then cut-off branches of the current itself and therefore can have nothing to do with its structure.

In an analysis of transient wind-driven circulations the author[3] found that narrow intense coastal currents are generated as purely inertial reactions to wind-produced shoreward transports of water and raised the question whether the Gulf Stream, the Kuroshio, and the Agulhas are not themselves such inertial reactions, requiring for their generation neither friction nor local wind stresses.[4] It is the purpose of the present article to show that the main features of the western currents in their generating areas can be accounted for by treating the motions as boundary-layer flows in which only pressure and inertial forces act. Since more is known of the detailed structure of the Gulf Stream than of the other currents, the discussion is confined to it. Specifically, an explanation is advanced for the Florida Current, that portion of the Gulf Stream system in which most of the flow is generated and in which the current remains parallel to the coast. After the current leaves the continental slope, it may no longer be treated as a boundary layer nor even as a steady-state flow.

Construction of the Model.—The solution to the ocean circulation problem presented by Munk is deemed to be valid at the outer or seaward edge of the Florida Current. Here, as Munk has shown, the flow is essentially determined by the balance of the pressure, Coriolis, and wind-stress forces. As the coast is approached, the velocity gradients increase and both the frictional forces and the nonlinear field accelerations become large. One may satisfy the boundary condition of vanishing normal velocity either by invoking friction or by taking into account the nonlinear field accelerations.[5] Since the frictional forces are important only at distances from the coast small in comparison with the width of the boundary current (unless excessively large eddy viscosities are assumed), whereas the field accelerations are large across the entire current, the latter course is adopted.

An essential property of the Florida Current is its intense baroclinicity. An isotherm at the center of the mean thermocline, say the 10° C. isotherm, rises from a depth of 900 m or so off South Carolina to nearly the surface at the coast. Accompanying the large horizontal density gradients are strong density currents which diminish rapidly to zero below the 10° isotherm. We adopt as the simplest system embodying the above properties an ocean consisting of two homogeneous incompressible layers. From a mean of actual soundings we take the density difference to be 2.0×10^{-3} gm cm^{-3}, and for comparison of theory with observation we identify the interface with the 10° isotherm. Disregarding seasonal or intraseasonal variations, we suppose the motion to be steady and to be confined to the upper layer. The implied assumption, which is made for simplicity and for lack of good evidence to the contrary, is that there is little frictional momentum transfer across the thermocline and that the deep waters have been brought to rest through the action of bottom friction.

The Munk theory prescribes the total volume transported by each section of the Florida Current. These transports will be regarded as the basic data of our problem. Since, however, their computed values depend on a very imperfectly known wind-stress distribution over the entire ocean, we shall instead use observed values for the purpose of testing our theory.

Although the coast line in the Florida Straits–Cape Hatteras generating region is crescent-shaped, the curvature effects induced in the stream are small. For example, that part of the vertical component of relative vorticity which is due to curvature is found to be negligible in comparison to the part which is due to shear. The motion may therefore be described in a rectangular co-ordinate system in which the coast line coincides with one of the axes. We place the y-axis at the coast line, or, more precisely, at the edge of the continental shelf, and the x-axis at right angles and pointing seaward. With slight approximation we may assume that the y-axis points north and the x-axis east.

Derivation of the Governing Equations.—Referring now to the upper layer, we let p be the pressure, ρ the density, u the x-component of velocity, v the y-component of velocity, and h the depth. The Coriolis parameter is denoted by f. Following Rossby,[6] we ignore the unimportant kinematic effects of the earth's curvature by assuming the motion to be planar, but retain the important dynamic effects associated with the latitudinal variability of f by allowing f to be a function of y. The equations of motion and continuity for the upper layer then take the simple forms

$$u\frac{\partial u}{\partial x} + v\frac{\partial u}{\partial y} - fv = -\frac{\partial}{\partial x}\left(\frac{p}{\rho}\right), \tag{1}$$

$$u\frac{\partial v}{\partial x} + v\frac{\partial v}{\partial y} + fu = -\frac{\partial}{\partial y}\left(\frac{p}{\rho}\right), \tag{2}$$

$$\frac{\partial}{\partial x}(hu) + \frac{\partial}{\partial y}(hv) = 0. \tag{3}$$

Here, in accordance with our assumptions, no frictional forces are included.

If the velocity is to be zero in the lower layer, the pressure must be constant in a horizontal plane. Denoting quantities in the lower layer by primes, we have, hydrostatically,

$$p' = g\rho h + g\rho' h' + \text{constant},$$

$$p = g\rho(h + h') + \text{constant},$$

in horizontal planes, whence

$$\frac{p}{\rho} + \text{constant} = g\left(1 - \frac{\rho}{\rho'}\right) h \equiv g'h. \tag{4}$$

Cross-differentiation of the equations of motion and combination with the equation of continuity yield the vorticity equation,

$$u \frac{\partial}{\partial x}(\zeta + f) + v \frac{\partial}{\partial y}(\zeta + f) = (\zeta + f)\left(u \frac{\partial h}{\partial x} + v \frac{\partial h}{\partial y}\right),$$

or

$$u \frac{\partial}{\partial x}\left(\frac{\zeta + f}{h}\right) + v \frac{\partial}{\partial y}\left(\frac{\zeta + f}{h}\right) = 0, \tag{5}$$

where ζ is the relative vertical component of vorticity $\partial v/\partial x - \partial u/\partial y$. This equation states that the potential vorticity $(\zeta + f)/h$ is conserved along a streamline. From the equation of continuity we may introduce the volume transport stream function ψ defined by

$$hu = -\frac{\partial \psi}{\partial y}, \qquad hv = \frac{\partial \psi}{\partial x}, \tag{6}$$

and equation (5) may be written in the form

$$\frac{1}{h}\left[\frac{\partial}{\partial x}\left(\frac{1}{h}\frac{\partial \psi}{\partial x}\right) + \frac{\partial}{\partial y}\left(\frac{1}{h}\frac{\partial \psi}{\partial y}\right)\right] = F(\psi), \tag{7}$$

where F is a function of ψ to be determined.

A second equation relating ψ and h is the Bernoulli equation. Multiplying equation (1) by u and equation (2) by v and adding, we obtain, with the substitution of $p/\rho = g'h + \text{constant}$,

$$u \frac{\partial}{\partial x}\left(\frac{u^2 + v^2}{2} + g'h\right) + v \frac{\partial}{\partial y}\left(\frac{u^2 + v^2}{2} + g'h\right) = 0, \tag{8}$$

or

$$\frac{1}{2}\left[\left(\frac{1}{h}\frac{\partial \psi}{\partial x}\right)^2 + \left(\frac{1}{h}\frac{\partial \psi}{\partial y}\right)^2\right] + g'h = G(\psi). \tag{9}$$

Here G is another function of ψ to be determined.

The inertial boundary layer is the region in which the nonlinear field accelerations are comparable in magnitude with the Coriolis and pressure forces per unit mass. To estimate the orders of magnitude of the terms in equations (7) and (9), we introduce the characteristic magnitudes of u and v, U and V, the characteristic width of the current ϵ, and the characteristic length of the current L into the continuity equation (3) and the vorticity equation (5). From the first we obtain $U/V \sim \epsilon/L$, and from the second $V/L\epsilon \sim df/dy \equiv \beta$. Here the symbol "$\sim$" denotes equality in order of magnitude. Combining the two relations, we get $\epsilon^2 \sim U/\beta$. But U is the characteristic externally prescribed lateral current velocity at the outer edge of the Florida Current, i.e., $U \sim 10$ cm sec^{-1}; L is of the order 10^8 cm; and $\beta \sim 10^{-13}$ cm^{-1} sec^{-1}. Hence $\epsilon \sim (10/10^{-13})^{1/2} \sim 10^7$ cm; $V \sim LU/\epsilon \sim 10^2$ cm sec^{-1}; and within the Florida Current $|v| \gg |u|$, $|\partial v/\partial x \div \partial u/\partial y| \sim VL/U\epsilon \sim L^2/\epsilon^2 \sim 10^2 \gg 1$. Equations (7) and (9) may therefore be replaced by

$$\frac{1}{h}\left(\frac{\partial v}{\partial x} + f\right) = F(\psi) \tag{10}$$

and

$$\frac{v^2}{2} + g'h = G(\psi), \tag{11}$$

respectively, v being given by the second of equations (6).

Evaluation of $F(\psi)$ and $G(\psi)$; Determination of Empirical Functions.—To evaluate $F(\psi)$ and $G(\psi)$, we introduce the outer boundary conditions and utilize the fact that the highest-order terms in the equations of motion (1) and (2) as well as in equations (5) and (8) become negligible at the outer boundary ($x = \infty$). Denoting quantities at this boundary by a bar, we obtain, from equations (2), (4), and (6),

$$\bar{u} = -\frac{1}{\bar{h}}\frac{d\bar{\psi}}{dy} = -\frac{g'}{f}\frac{d\bar{h}}{dy} \tag{12}$$

and, from equations (10) and (11),

$$\frac{f}{\bar{h}} = F(\psi), \tag{13}$$

$$g'\bar{h} = G(\psi). \tag{14}$$

At the outer boundary the quantity $\bar{\psi}$ is a prescribed function of y. Hence integration of equation (12) gives $\bar{h}$ as a function of y and therefore also of $\bar{\psi}$. But, at the outer limit, both $f/\bar{h}$ in equation (13) and $g'\bar{h}$ in equation (14) are also functions of y and therefore of $\bar{\psi}$. In this way the functions $F(\psi)$ and $G(\psi)$ are determined along the outer boundary and consequently at every point in the interior region connected with the outer boundary by a streamline. Since in the present formulation of the problem all interior points are so connected, the problem of the determination of $F(\psi)$ and $G(\psi)$ is solved in principle. The actual forms of the functions will depend on the particular form taken for $\bar{\psi}(y)$.

The parabolic function

$$\bar{\psi} = \bar{\psi}_0 - \gamma(y - y_0)^2 \tag{15}$$

corresponds in Munk's theory to the requirement that the transport into the Gulf Stream change sign approximately where the mean zonal wind changes sign. The function fits the observed distribution of $\bar{\psi}$ quite well for $y < y_0$, y_0 being the point at which the transport reaches its maximum value $\bar{\psi}_0$. To evaluate the constants $\bar{\psi}_0$ and γ, we take $\psi = 0$ at the coast, so that $\bar{\psi}$ becomes the volume transport of the current, and we take the zero point of y to be midway between the Florida Straits and Cape Hatteras ($y = y_0$), a distance of 700 km measured along the coast from each. The geostrophically calculated transport in the Florida Straits is approximately 30×10^6 m^3 sec^{-1}, and the increase from there to Cape Hatteras is approximately 50×10^6 m^3 sec^{-1}.[7, 8] Hence $\bar{\psi}_0 = 80 \times 10^6$ m^3 sec^{-1}, and γ has the value $50 \times 10^6 \div (14 \times 10^5)^2 = 2.55 \times 10^{-5}$ m sec^{-1}.

It is sufficiently accurate to take f a linear function of y. Setting

$$f = f_0 + \beta(y - y_0), \tag{16}$$

we have $f_0 = 0.84 \times 10^{-4}$ sec^{-1} and $\beta = 1.8 \times 10^{-11}$ m^{-1} sec^{-1}.

With the substitution of equations (15) and (16), equation (12) may be integrated directly, to give for $\bar{h}$

$$\bar{h}^2 = \bar{h}_0{}^2 - \frac{2\gamma f_0}{g'}(y - y_0)^2 - \frac{4\gamma\beta}{3g'}(y - y_0)^3, \tag{17}$$

or, in view of equation (15),

$$\bar{h}^2 = \bar{h}_0{}^2 - \frac{2f_0}{g'}(\bar{\psi}_0 - \bar{\psi}) + \frac{4\gamma\beta}{3g'}\left(\frac{\bar{\psi}_0 - \bar{\psi}}{\gamma}\right)^{3/2} \tag{18}$$

This expression for $\bar{h}$ is now substituted in equation (14) and the bar removed from $\bar{\psi}$. We obtain for $G(\psi)$

$$G(\psi) = g'\left[\bar{h}_0{}^2 - \frac{2f_0}{g'}(\bar{\psi}_0 - \psi) + \frac{4\beta}{3g'\gamma^{1/2}}(\bar{\psi}_0 - \psi)^{3/2}\right]^{1/2}. \tag{19}$$

The function $F(\psi)$ may be obtained by a similar process, or, more simply, as follows: We differentiate equation (14) with respect to ψ along the outer boundary thus:

$$\frac{dG}{d\psi} = \frac{dG}{dy}\frac{dy}{d\psi} = g'\frac{d\bar{h}}{dy}\frac{dy}{d\psi},$$

and substitute from equation (12)

$$\frac{dy}{d\psi} = \frac{f}{g'\bar{h}}\frac{dy}{dh}.$$

The result is

$$\frac{dG}{d\psi} = \frac{f}{\bar{h}} = F, \tag{20}$$

which holds for all y and therefore for all ψ.[9]

Solution of Equations.—Equations (10) and (11) are solved as follows: Observing that y enters only parametrically, we replace x as independent variable by ψ. Then $\partial v/\partial x = (\partial v/\partial\psi)(\partial\psi/\partial x) = hv(\partial v/\partial\psi)$, and equation (10) becomes

$$hv\frac{\partial v}{\partial\psi} + f = hF(\psi).$$

We eliminate v by utilizing equation (11) differentiated with respect to ψ:

$$v\frac{\partial v}{\partial \psi} + g'\frac{\partial h}{\partial \psi} = \frac{dG}{d\psi}.$$

The final equation is

$$\frac{\partial h}{\partial \psi} - \frac{f}{g'h} = \frac{1}{g'}\left(\frac{dG}{d\psi} - F\right) = 0. \tag{21}$$

Its solution, subject to the boundary condition $h = \bar{h}(y)$ at $\psi = \bar{\psi}(y)$, is

$$h^2 = \bar{h}^2 + \frac{2f}{g'}(\psi - \bar{\psi}), \tag{22}$$

which is recognized as a form of the statement that v is geostrophic. Indeed, the above relation could have been derived directly from equations (1) and (6) by applying the boundary-layer approximations which were justified in the derivation of equations (10) and (11). We have merely shown here that these approximations have been used consistently.

The velocity v is obtained as a function of ψ and y from equations (11), (19), and (22), and x is obtained as a function of ψ and y by solving the equation

$$dx = \frac{d\psi}{hv} \tag{23}$$

which requires only a numerical quadrature. The boundary condition here is $x = 0$ at $\psi = 0$.

Evaluation of $\bar{h}_0$ and the Phenomenon of Separation.—Before the integrations can be performed, it is necessary to determine the constant of integration in equation (19). This quantity is the depth of the upper layer at the latitude of maximum current transport. A theoretical value may be obtained by the following heuristic argument: We observe first that the flow can no longer be regarded as an inertial boundary flow at latitudes greater than y_0. This is so because fluid columns which enter the stream south of y_0 and leave it to the north conserve both the stream function and the potential vorticity; but the potential vorticity at the outer boundary increases monotonically with y through y_0, whereas the stream function increases south of y_0 and decreases north. We must therefore drop the assumption that $\bar{\zeta} \ll f$ in the expression $(\bar{\zeta} + f)/\bar{h}$ for the potential vorticity at the outer boundary; but this means that the current, defined as the region in which the field accelerations are appreciable, must leave the coast at $y = y_0$ and go out to sea. On the assumption that the current remains coherent because of rotational stability, it follows that the shoreward edge must do likewise. Since the interface separating the upper from the lower homogeneous layer also separates the region of motion from the region of no motion, we have the result that the interface must rise to the surface of the ocean at $x = 0$, $y = y_0$ and thenceforth extend out to sea as a front dividing the Gulf Stream from the slope water. That the interface cannot come to the surface at the coast for $y < y_0$ may be seen from equation (22). Setting $\psi = 0$ and differentiating with respect to y, we obtain, with the aid of equation (12),

$$\frac{d\bar{h}_{\text{coast}}^2}{dy} = \frac{-2\beta\bar{\psi}}{g'} < 0,$$

which shows that $\bar{h}$ has to decrease monotonically as long as the current continues to flow along the coast.

In view of the foregoing analysis, we may state that $h = 0$ at $x = 0$, $y = y_0$. Substituting $\psi = 0$ and $h = 0$ at $y = y_0$ in equation (22), we obtain for $\bar{h}_0$ the value

$$\bar{h}_0 = \left(\frac{2f_0\bar{\psi}_0}{g'}\right)^{1/2} = 820 \text{ m},$$

which compares well with the observed mean value of 900 m given by Iselin[10] for the depth of the 10° isotherm at the offshore edge of the Gulf Stream in the vicinity of Cape Hatteras.

We note that in our theory the phenomenon of separation does not require the presence of a protrusion of the coast line such as actually exists in both the Gulf Stream and the Kuroshio case. It would be of interest to see whether this conclusion is verified by model experiment. It may be shown that an analogous phenomenon can be expected to occur in the case of the more easily modeled ocean consisting of a single homogeneous layer.

Comparison of Theory with Observation.—The results of the integrations are represented in Figures 1(a, b) and 2. Figure 1(a) depicts contours of the depth h of the upper of the two homogeneous layers at intervals of 100 m, together with the volume-transport streamlines ψ = *constant* drawn at intervals of ten million cubic meters per second. Since the x-scale of motion is very small compared to the y-

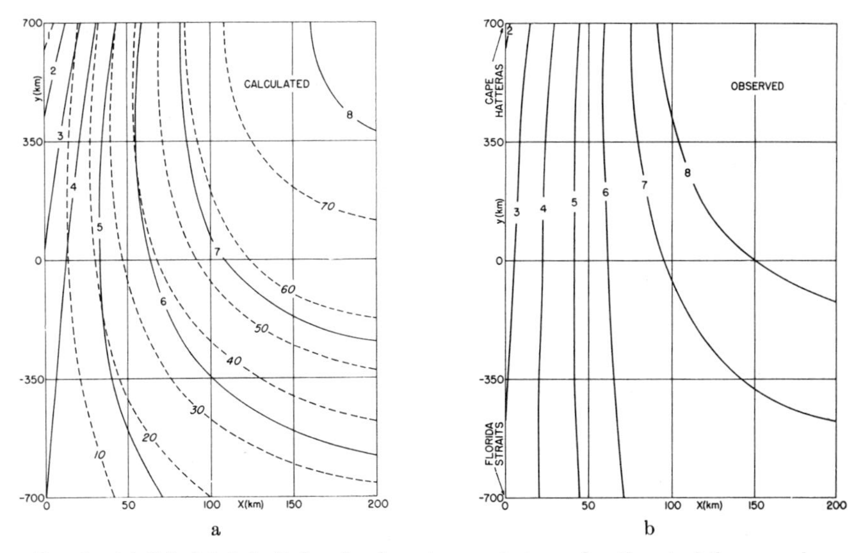

FIG. 1.—(a) Calculated depth h and volume transport stream function ψ of the upper layer. The contours of h (*solid lines*) are drawn for each 100 m, and the streamlines for each ten million cubic meters per second. (b) Schematic chart of the observed mean depths of the 10° C. isotherm.

scale, the former has been exaggerated in the diagrams by the factor 5. For comparison with observation the depth contours of the 10° isotherm taken from Iselin's article,[10] together with his Florida Current temperature cross-sections, were used to construct Figure 1(*b*) a contour chart of the 10° isotherm in which the edge of the continental shelf is represented by the y-axis and distances normal and parallel to the edge by the x- and y-co-ordinates, respectively. Because of the slope of the edge of the continental shelf and because of the complicated thermal structure near the surface at the inshore edge of the current, this chart must be considered as merely schematic. It will be seen, nevertheless, that the agreement in general between the two charts is good. The principal disagreement is in the Florida Straits. Here the lack of difluence in the observed contours, which has no counterpart in the calculated contours, is probably due to the offshore constraint of the Great Bahama Bank.

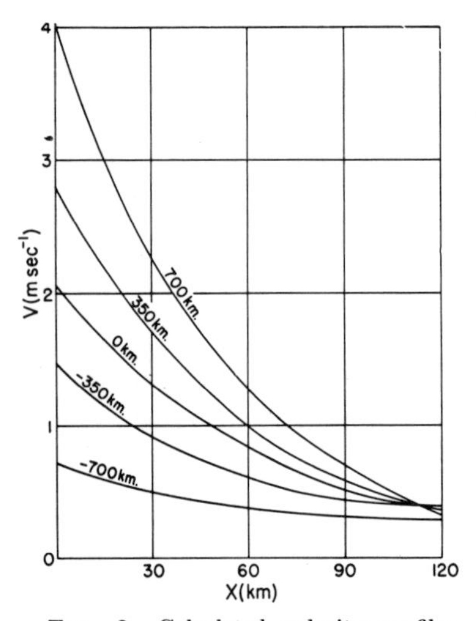

FIG. 2.—Calculated velocity profiles across the Florida Current at various latitudes y measured along the coast from a point midway between the Florida Straits and Cape Hatteras.

The v-velocity profiles across the current are shown in Figure 2 for various values of y. At a given latitude, the maximum velocities are found at the inshore edge of the current and reach a value of 4.06 m sec^{-1} at Cape Hatteras. These are, as would be expected in the absence of boundary friction, on the upward side of the observed range of 2.00–2.50 m sec^{-1} normally found in the swiftest part of the current (Iselin and Fuglister[11]). The location of the highest velocities agrees with the observation that they are "confined to a relatively narrow band 10 to 15 miles wide situated near the left or inshore edge of the current."

Application of the Geostrophic Approximation; Concluding Remarks.—The general theory which has been presented takes a particularly simple mathematical form when the quasi-geostrophic approximation is made, i.e., when both u and v are assumed to be geostrophic and when $\bar{h}$ varies linearly with y: $\bar{h} = \bar{h}_0 + \mu(y - y_0)$. In this case equation (11) becomes redundant, and equation (10) takes the form

$$\frac{1}{h}\left[\frac{\partial}{\partial x}\left(\frac{g'}{f}\frac{\partial h}{\partial x}\right) + f\right] = F(h), \tag{24}$$

where

$$F(h) = \frac{f}{\bar{h}} = \frac{f_0 + \beta(y - y_0)}{\bar{h}_0 + \mu(y - y_0)} = \frac{f_0 + \beta(h - \bar{h}_0)/\mu}{h}. \tag{25}$$

We thus obtain

$$\frac{\partial^2 h}{\partial x^2} - \frac{f\beta}{g'\mu}h = \frac{f}{g'}\left(f_0 - f - \frac{\beta\bar{h}_0}{\mu}\right) = -\frac{f_0\beta}{g'\mu}\bar{h}(y),$$

the solution of which, subject to the condition that $h = \bar{h}$ at $x = \infty$, is

$$h = Ae^{-x/\lambda} + \bar{h}(y), \tag{26}$$

where $\lambda^2 = g'\mu/f\beta$. The constant A is determined by specifying the volume transport $\bar{\psi}_0$ at $y = y_0$. We have, geostrophically,

$$\bar{\psi}_0 = \int_0^\infty h \frac{g'}{f} \frac{\partial h}{\partial x} dx = \frac{g'}{2f} (\bar{h}^2 - h_c^2),$$

where h_c is the (necessarily constant) value of h at $x = 0$. With the condition $h = h_c$ at $x = 0$, equation (26) becomes

$$h = \bar{h}(y) - (\bar{h} - h_c)e^{-x/\lambda}.$$

The width of the current is of the order $\lambda = (g'\mu/f\beta)^{1/2}$. The quantity $g'\mu/f$ is the magnitude $|\bar{u}| = (g'/f)\ \partial\bar{h}/\partial y$ of the lateral velocity at the outer boundary. Hence $\lambda = (\bar{u}/\beta)^{1/2}$. It is thus seen that the Gulf Stream is a phenomenon that depends in an essential way on the variation of the Coriolis parameter with latitude. Substituting observed values for $\bar{u}$ and β, we find that λ is about 50 km. In general, it may be said that the geostrophic approximation predicts the rough character of the current but does not predict all details. Thus in the geostrophic theory h is constant along the coast, and therefore no phenomenon such as separation can occur.

In conclusion, we mention two extensions of the theory which suggest themselves. First, the boundary-layer technique which has been presented here can readily be extended to a continuously stratified ocean. In this case, one prescribes, in place of the depth of the upper homogeneous layer, the continuous density distribution at the outer edge of the boundary current. Second, an internal frictional boundary layer should be introduced to reduce the velocities to zero on the inshore edge of the currents. This can be done only if one knows something of the nature of the eddy viscosity.

The author wishes to acknowledge his debt to Mr. Henry Stommel, of the Woods Hole Oceanographic Institution, from whom he gained much of his knowledge of the ocean circulations and in whose inspiring company the Gulf Stream problem was discussed over and over again until eventually it may be said to have solved itself.

* This study was sponsored jointly by the Office of Naval Research and the Geophysics Research Directorate of the Air Force Cambridge Research Center, under Contract No. N-6-ori-139 Task Order I with the Office of Naval Research.

[1] H. Stommel, "The Westward Intensification of Wind-driven Ocean Currents," *Trans. Am. Geophys. Union*, **29**, 202–206, 1948.

[2] W. H. Munk, "On the Wind-driven Ocean Circulation," *J. Meteorol.*, **7**, No. 2, 79–93, 1950.

[3] J. G. Charney, "Generation of Ocean Currents by Wind," *J. Marine Research*, Vol. **14**, No. 4, 1955 (to be published).

[4] The same view has also been expressed by Stommel (1954) in a privately printed article entitled "Why Do Our Ideas about the Ocean Circulation Have Such a Peculiarly Dream-like Quality?", and N. P. Fofonoff (*J. Marine Research*, **2**, 254–262, 1954) has given an example of a sharp boundary current occurring as part of a free circulation in an inclosed homogeneous ocean of constant depth with a variable Coriolis parameter.

[5] H. U. Sverdrup, "Wind-driven Currents in a Baroclinic Ocean, with Application to the Equatorial Currents of the Eastern Pacific," these PROCEEDINGS, **33**, 318–326, 1947.

[6] C.-G. Rossby and collaborators, "Relation between Variations in the Intensity of the Zonal

Circulation of the Atmosphere and the Displacements of the Semi-permanent Centers of Action," *J. Marine Research,* **2,** 38–55, 1939.

[7] C. O. Iselin, "Preliminary Report on Long Period Variations in the Transport of the Gulf Stream System," *Papers Phys. Oceanog. Meteorol. Mass. Inst. Technol. and Woods Hole Oceanog. Inst.*, Vol. **8,** No. 1, 1940.

[8] H. U. Sverdrup, M. W. Johnson, and R. H. Fleming, *The Oceans* (New York: Prentice-Hall Inc., 1942).

[9] Relation (20), which holds quite generally for steady frictionless flows, was pointed out to the author by C.-G. Rossby.

[10] C. O. Iselin, "A Study of the Circulation of the Western North Atlantic," *Papers Phys. Oceanog. Meteorol. Mass. Inst. Technol. and Woods Hole Oceanog. Inst.*, Vol. **4,** No. 4, 1936.

[11] C. O. Iselin and F. C. Fuglister, "Some Recent Developments in the Study of the Gulf Stream," *J. Marine Research,* **7,** N. 3, 317–329, 1950.

On the wind-driven ocean circulation

G. W. Morgan

Reprinted with permission from
Tellus
Volume 8, Number 3,
pages 301 through 320, 1956

On the Wind-Driven Ocean Circulation[1]

By G. W. MORGAN, Brown University, Providence

(Manuscript received February 8, revised June 5, 1956)

Abstract

Some aspects of existing theories of the wind-driven ocean circulation are examined with particular emphasis on the question of the need for the inclusion of lateral eddy viscosity to provide a mechanism for balancing the applied wind torque. A new model is proposed according to which the ocean is divided into a southern and a northern portion, attention being restricted to the former which is itself subdivided into an interior region and a boundary region adjacent to the western shore. The equations of motion in terms of spherical coordinates are formally integrated over depth for both a homogeneous and a two-layer ocean. Approximate equations analogous to those used in existing theories are proposed for the interior region. Conditions in the boundary region are considered in an effort to determine the relative importance of the various terms in the equations. Based on these considerations approximate equations are derived for the boundary region. These imply the predominance of the pressure terms, the nonlinear inertia terms and the terms arising from the variation of the Coriolis parameter with latitude.

The approximate equations are transformed to surface coordinates and are applied to the homogeneous ocean and a two-layer ocean subjected to a simple wind distribution, yielding reasonable results. It is shown that the variation of the Coriolis parameter plays a fundamental role in the formation of the stream on the western shore. Simple physical interpretations of the results are presented including an explanation of the facts that no similar stream can be formed on the eastern shore and that the variation of depth in a two-layer ocean, when the Coriolis parameter is assumed constant, cannot give rise to an intense stream. Appropriate curves illustrating the dependence of the solutions on certain dimensionless parameters are given. When applied to the North Atlantic the theory gives reasonable results for the Gulf Stream north to, say, Cape Hatteras.

1. Introduction

Existing theories of the wind-driven circulation in closed ocean basins (SVERDRUP, 1947; MUNK, 1950) are based on the assumption that the principal features of the flow pattern are the result of the balance between wind, Coriolis, lateral friction and pressure forces and that all other contributions to the dynamic equations are, for purposes of an approximate investigation, negligible. This assumption leads to a linear problem, an approximate solution of which is obtained most conveniently by applying boundary layer analysis to the vorticity equation (MUNK and CARRIER, 1950). Although the circulation which is predicted is, at least qualitatively, very reasonable, the theory has been criticized especially on the grounds that the value of the coefficient of lateral eddy viscosity must be chosen empirically, and further, that the value which gives the proper width to the intense current on the western shore is considerably larger than that indicated by other, independent considerations.

In the following, other aspects of the abovementioned theories are considered and attention is devoted to the question of the importance of the lateral eddy viscosity. It has previously been argued that this must be included in every steady-state theory because it provides the forces of friction on the sides of the basin which give rise to the torque that

[1] Contribution No. 811 from the Woods Hole Oceanographic Institution.

must be present to balance the total torque exerted on the ocean by the wind. This problem is discussed in Section 2 where an equation for the balance of total moment of momentum about the center of mass of the ocean is derived and it is seen that this consideration alone is not sufficient to determine whether friction is required in the moment balance.

In Section 3 the equation of vorticity in terms of spherical coordinates is formally integrated over the depth of a layer of water which is considered to have uniform density (either the total ocean depth, if one deals with a homogeneous model, or the depth of the upper layer in a two-layer model). Approximate equations which apply to the interior region of the ocean and stipulate the predominance of wind, Coriolis, and pressure forces are derived in Section 4. In Section 5 the conditions in the boundary region in which an intense current is expected are discussed and we return to the problem of the need for including lateral eddy viscosity. Based on this discussion a model is proposed according to which the ocean is divided into a southern and a northern region. Attention is confined to the former which is again divided into an interior region, to which the equations derived in Section 4 apply, and a boundary region, adjacent to the western shore, for which approximate equations are derived by means of boundary layer analysis. These imply the predominance of the pressure terms, the non-linear inertia terms, and the terms arising from the variation of the Coriolis parameter with latitude, friction being neglected.[1]

The approximate equations are transformed to surface coordinates in Section 6 and are applied to a homogeneous ocean in Section 7. The theory predicts an intense current flowing northward along the western shore. The reason for the existence of this current from a physical point of view is discussed and it is shown why no similar current can exist on the eastern shore.

In Section 8 the theory is applied to the upper layer of a two-layer ocean. The role of a certain parameter involving the depth of the layer, the magnitude of the westward volume transport into the boundary region, the south-north dimension of the basin, the reduced gravity constant, and the variation of the Coriolis parameter with latitude, is studied. A proof is given that the variation of the Coriolis parameter is essential to the formation of an intense current even in a two-layer system. Numerical solutions are presented and it is concluded that, for reasonable values of the physical quantities involved, the barotropic and baroclinic models are not basically different as far as the formation of the stream is concerned. When applied to the North Atlantic the theory predicts the correct order of magnitude for the width of the Gulf Stream.

2. Moment of Momentum Balance

It has frequently been asserted (e.g. MONTGOMERY, 1940) that, for steady-state conditions, friction must be present on the bounding surfaces of the basin to provide the torque required to balance the total torque applied by the wind. Since it has been held reasonable to assume that the friction on the bottom is negligible, this argument has led to the conclusion that lateral eddy viscosity must be included in the equations of motion in order to give rise to a shear stress on the sides of the basin. In view of the obvious importance of this question, it will be examined in the following. The physical quantity of interest is the total moment of momentum about the center of mass, the momentum referring to the velocity recorder by an observer who is fixed to the earth. For steady-state conditions this moment must be constant.

The equation of motion is

$$\varrho \frac{Dq}{Dt} + \varrho 2\boldsymbol{\Omega} \times \boldsymbol{q} + \varrho\boldsymbol{\Omega} \times (\boldsymbol{\Omega} \times \boldsymbol{r}) = = -\nabla p + \varrho \nabla \chi' + \boldsymbol{F} \qquad (2.1)$$

where q is the velocity of a particle as seen by an observer fixed to the earth, D/Dt is the material derivative, ϱ is the density (not necessarily uniform), $\boldsymbol{\Omega}$ is the earth's angular

[1] The probability that viscosity is unimportant in the Gulf Stream was suggested by H. Stommel in a discussion following formal papers delivered at the June 1954 Convocation at Woods Hole (the complete proceedings of which are to be published as a supplement to the Journal of Marine Research, Vol. 14, No. 4, Dec. 31, 1955), and in a privately printed pamphlet entitled "Why do our ideas about the ocean circulation have such a peculiarly dream-like quality?", April 1954.

rotation vector, $\boldsymbol{r}$ is the position vector of the particle with respect to the center of the earth and with respect to a coordinate system which rotates with the earth, p is the pressure, χ' is the gravitational potential, and $\boldsymbol{F}$ is the net force on a unit volume due to eddy viscosity and can be written $\nabla \cdot \sigma$ where σ denotes the stress dyad minus the contribution of the pressure p.

The equation of conservation of mass is

$$\frac{\partial \varrho}{\partial t} + \operatorname{div} \varrho \boldsymbol{q} = 0. \qquad (2.2)$$

Set

$$\nabla \chi' - \boldsymbol{\Omega} \times (\boldsymbol{\Omega} \times \boldsymbol{r}) = \nabla \chi' - \nabla \left(\frac{1}{2} \Omega^2 \tilde{\omega}^2\right) \equiv \nabla \chi \qquad (2.3)$$

where $\tilde{\omega}$ is the perpendicular distance of a point from the axis of rotation of the earth, Ω is the absolute value of $\boldsymbol{\Omega}$ and χ is the apparent gravitational potential. Carrying out the vector multiplication of the resulting equation with $\boldsymbol{r}_c$, the position vector of a point with respect to the center of mass, and integrating over the total volume of the ocean, one has

$$\int_V \varrho \boldsymbol{r}_c \times \frac{D\boldsymbol{q}}{Dt} dV + \int_V \varrho \boldsymbol{r}_c \times (2\boldsymbol{\Omega} \times \boldsymbol{q})\, dV = - \int_V \boldsymbol{r}_c \times \nabla p dV + \int_V \varrho \boldsymbol{r}_c \times \nabla \chi dV + \int_V \boldsymbol{r}_c \times \nabla \sigma \cdot dV \qquad (2.4)$$

This equation can be transformed by making use of equation (2.2), the relations

$$\frac{D\boldsymbol{r}}{Dt} = \boldsymbol{q},$$

$$\int_V \varrho \frac{D\varphi}{Dt} dV = \frac{D}{Dt} \int_V \varrho \varphi dV, \qquad (2.5)$$

φ being any arbitrary continuous function with continuous first derivatives, and the transformation formulae relating volume and surface integrals, to give

$$\frac{D}{Dt} \int_V \boldsymbol{r}_c + \varrho \boldsymbol{q} dV + \int_V \boldsymbol{r}_c \times \varrho\, (2\,\boldsymbol{\Omega} \times \boldsymbol{q}) dV = \int_V \varrho \boldsymbol{r}_c \times \nabla \chi dV - \int_S \boldsymbol{r}_c \times \boldsymbol{n} p dS + \int_S \boldsymbol{r}_c \times \boldsymbol{T} dS \qquad (2.6)$$

where S is the surface enclosing the volume V, $\boldsymbol{n}$ is the unit outer normal vector on S, and $\boldsymbol{T} \equiv \boldsymbol{n} \cdot \sigma$ and denotes that portion of the surface traction which is due to the frictional mechanism. It should be noted that equation (2.6) holds irrespective of the particular nature of the eddy viscosity (or molecular viscosity), the only additional requirement for its derivation being the symmetry of the stress dyad.

The left-hand side of equation (2.6) represents the rate of change of moment of momentum and consists of the rate of change as seen by an observer fixed to the earth and the contribution by the Coriolis forces. The right-hand side represents the moment of all external forces, the gravitational attraction, the pressure on the surfaces and the forces arising from viscosity. The last integral may be split into two portions, one involving integration over the free surface and thus representing the moment due to the wind, the other involving integration over the ocean bottom and sides. The contribution of the pressures to the moment is principally due to the fact that the free surface is disturbed by the motion and that the moments due to the pressures on the sides will then not, in general, add to zero. If one deals with a circular basin having a vertical shore and uniform depth, then the moment due to the pressures acting on the shore will be very small because the center of mass will be very close to the geometrical center.

For a steady-state solution the first term on the left of equation (2.6) must vanish. The contribution of the body force to the moment is negligible. Thus the moment balance involves the contributions of the Coriolis force, the pressure, the wind, and the friction on the shores and bottom, and it is seen that no immediate conclusion can be drawn from this consideration alone concerning the need for including friction on the sides, even if friction on the bottom is neglected from the start. The moment created by the wind may possibly be balanced by the Coriolis and pressure moments, or by the former alone if the basin is circular.

The preceding considerations in no way prove that lateral friction is not required; they only demonstrate that the question cannot be decided on the basis of moment balance alone. The problem will be discussed from a different point of view in Section 5.

3. Equations of Motion in Spherical Coordinates

Since an analytical investigation of the three-dimensional problem is prohibitively complicated, we follow the usual procedure of confining our attention to the integrals over depth of the velocity components and of the vorticity.

Using the spherical coordinates (r, ϑ, φ), the origin being at the center of the earth and ϑ being the colatitude, and corresponding velocity components q_1, q_2, q_3, the momentum equations are

$$\frac{\partial q_1}{\partial t} + \text{non linear terms} - 2\, q_3 \Omega \sin\vartheta = -\frac{1}{\varrho}\frac{\partial p}{\partial r} - g + F_1 \tag{3.1}$$

$$\frac{\partial q_2}{\partial t} + q_1 \frac{\partial q_2}{\partial r} + \frac{q_2}{r}\frac{\partial q_2}{\partial \vartheta} + \frac{q_3}{r\sin\vartheta}\frac{\partial q_2}{\partial \varphi} + \frac{q_1 q_2}{r} - \frac{q_3^2 \cot\vartheta}{r} - 2\, q_3 \Omega \cos\vartheta = -\frac{1}{\varrho}\frac{1}{r}\frac{\partial p}{\partial \vartheta} + F_2 \tag{3.2}$$

$$\frac{\partial q_3}{\partial t} + q_1 \frac{\partial q_3}{\partial r} + \frac{q_2}{r}\frac{\partial q_3}{\partial \vartheta} + \frac{q_3}{r\sin\vartheta}\frac{\partial q_3}{\partial \varphi} + \frac{q_1 q_3}{r} + \frac{q_2 q_3}{r}\cot\vartheta + 2 q_2 \Omega \cos\vartheta + 2 q_1 \Omega \sin\vartheta = -\frac{1}{\varrho}\frac{1}{r\sin\vartheta}\frac{\partial p}{\partial \varphi} + F_3 \tag{3.3}$$

Here (F_1, F_2, F_3) denote the contributions of the eddy viscosity, g denotes the gravitational acceleration, and the centrifugal force terms which give rise to the ellipticity of the undisturbed free surface of the ocean have been neglected.

We shall make either of two assumptions concerning the distribution of density; a) we consider the "homogeneous" ocean which has uniform density everywhere and is subsequently assumed to be of uniform depth when undisturbed; b) we consider a "two-layer" ocean which consists of two superposed layers each of uniform density. In the latter case we shall be concerned only with the motion in the upper, lighter layer, and the equations of motion refer to that layer alone. Hence, in both cases, the equation expressing the conservation of mass is that for an incompressible fluid:

$$\frac{\partial}{\partial r}(r^2 \sin\vartheta\, q_1) + \frac{\partial}{\partial \vartheta}(r \sin\vartheta\, q_2) + \frac{\partial}{\partial \varphi}(r q_3) = 0 \tag{3.4}$$

The radial component of vorticity is

$$\zeta_1 = (\text{curl}\, \boldsymbol{q})_1 = \frac{1}{r^2 \sin\vartheta}\left[\frac{\partial}{\partial \vartheta}(r\sin\vartheta\, q_3) - \frac{\partial}{\partial \varphi}(r q_2)\right] \tag{3.5}$$

The first component equation of the vorticity equation is obtained by performing the operation appearing on the right side of (3.5) on equations (3.3) and (3.2) in the place of q_3 and q_2, respectively, and making use of equation (3.4):

$$\begin{aligned}
&\frac{\partial \zeta_1}{\partial t} + q_1 \frac{\partial \zeta_1}{\partial r} + \frac{q_2}{r}\frac{\partial \zeta_1}{\partial \vartheta} + \frac{q_3}{r\sin\vartheta}\frac{\partial \zeta_1}{\partial \varphi} + \\
&+ \frac{1}{r}\frac{\partial q_1}{\partial \vartheta}\frac{\partial q_3}{\partial r} + \frac{1}{r^2}\frac{\partial q_1}{\partial \vartheta} q_3 - \frac{1}{r\sin\vartheta}\frac{\partial q_1}{\partial \varphi}\frac{\partial q_2}{\partial r} - \\
&- \frac{1}{r^2 \sin\vartheta}\frac{\partial q_1}{\partial \varphi} q_2 + \frac{2}{r} q_1 \zeta_1 - \\
&- \frac{\zeta_1}{r^2 \sin\vartheta}\frac{\partial}{\partial r}(r^2 \sin\vartheta\, q_1) + \frac{4}{r}\Omega \cos\vartheta\, q_1 - \\
&- \frac{2}{r^2}\Omega \cot\vartheta \frac{\partial}{\partial r}(r^2 \sin\vartheta\, q_1) + \\
&+ \frac{2}{r}\Omega \sin\vartheta \frac{\partial q_1}{\partial \vartheta} - \frac{2}{r}\Omega \sin\vartheta\, q_2 = \\
&= \frac{1}{r^2 \sin\vartheta}\left[\frac{\partial}{\partial \vartheta}(r\sin\vartheta\, F_3) - \frac{\partial}{\partial \varphi}(r F_2)\right]
\end{aligned} \tag{3.6}$$

The rate of change of the first component of vorticity as we follow a particle is

$$\frac{D\zeta_1}{Dt} = \frac{\partial \zeta_1}{\partial t} + q_1 \frac{\partial \zeta_1}{\partial r} + \frac{q_2}{r}\frac{\partial \zeta_1}{\partial \vartheta} + \frac{q_3}{r\sin\vartheta}\frac{\partial \zeta_1}{\partial \varphi} \tag{3.7}$$

Note that this is not the same as the first component of $D\boldsymbol{\zeta}/Dt$, $\boldsymbol{\zeta}$ being the vorticity vector. We shall find it convenient to focus our attention on that portion of the rate of change of ζ_1 which is associated with the particle's horizontal motion only and therefore define

$$\frac{d}{dt} \equiv \frac{\partial}{\partial t} + \frac{q_2}{r}\frac{\partial}{\partial \vartheta} + \frac{q_3}{r\sin\vartheta}\frac{\partial}{\partial \varphi} \tag{3.8}$$

We now integrate equation (3.6) over the depth of the total ocean in case a) and over the upper layer in case b). In both cases the limits can be written $r = h_b(\vartheta, \varphi, t)$ on the bottom and $r = h_s(\vartheta, \varphi, t)$ on the free surface with h_b being constant in case a). Letting

$$f = 2\Omega\cos\vartheta \qquad (3.9)$$

and making use of (3.8) one obtains, after some manipulation

$$\int_{h_b}^{h_s} \frac{d\zeta_1}{dt}\,dr - (q_1\zeta_1)\Big|_{h_b}^{h_s} + 2\int_{h_b}^{h_s} q_1\frac{\partial\zeta_1}{\partial r}\,dr +$$

$$+ \int_{h_b}^{h_s}\left(\frac{1}{r}\frac{\partial q_1}{\partial\vartheta}\frac{\partial q_3}{\partial r} + \frac{1}{r^2}\frac{\partial q_1}{\partial\vartheta}q_3 - \frac{1}{r\sin\vartheta}\frac{\partial q_1}{\partial\varphi}\frac{\partial q_2}{\partial r} - \right.$$

$$\left. - \frac{1}{r^2\sin\vartheta}\frac{\partial q_1}{\partial\varphi}q_2\right)dr + \int_{h_b}^{h_s}\frac{df}{dt}\,dr - (q_1 f)\Big|_{h_b}^{h_s} +$$

$$+ 2\Omega\sin\vartheta\int_{h_b}^{h_s}\frac{1}{r}\frac{\partial q_1}{\partial\vartheta}\,dr =$$

$$= \frac{1}{\sin\vartheta}\int_{h_b}^{h_s}\frac{1}{r^2}\left[\frac{\partial}{\partial\vartheta}(r\sin\vartheta F_3) - \frac{\partial}{\partial\varphi}(rF_2)\right]dr \qquad (3.10)$$

where the symbol $(\ )\Big|_{h_b}^{h_s}$ stands for $(\ )_{r=h_s} - (\ )_{r=h_b}$.

We now evaluate the frictional terms in (3.10). Let

$$F_i = \frac{1}{\varrho}\frac{1}{r^2}\frac{\partial}{\partial r}\left(A_r r^2\frac{\partial q_i}{\partial r}\right) + F_i^*,\ i = 2, 3 \qquad (3.11)$$

where A_r denotes the radial eddy viscosity and F_2^*, F_3^* are used for the sake of brevity to represent the contributions due to the coefficient of lateral eddy viscosity A_L the magnitude of which is so far arbitrary. Assuming that A_r is independent of ϑ and φ and neglecting the variation of r within the range of the integration, one obtains for the right side of equation (3.10)

$$\frac{1}{\varrho}\frac{\cot\vartheta}{r}\left(A_r\frac{\partial q_3}{\partial r}\right)\Big|_{h_b}^{h_s} + \frac{1}{\varrho}\frac{1}{r}\left(A_r\frac{\partial^2 q_3}{\partial r\,\partial\vartheta}\right)\Big|_{h_b}^{h_s} -$$

$$- \frac{1}{\varrho}\frac{1}{r\sin\vartheta}\left(A_r\frac{\partial^2 q_2}{\partial r\,\partial\varphi}\right)\Big|_{h_b}^{h_s} +$$

$$+ \frac{1}{\sin\vartheta}\int_{h_b}^{h_s}\frac{1}{r^2}\left[\frac{\partial}{\partial\vartheta}(r\sin\vartheta F_3^*) - \frac{\partial}{\partial\varphi}(rF_2^*)\right]dr \qquad (3.12)$$

The pertinent components of shear stress are

$$\tau_{r\vartheta} = A_r\left(\frac{1}{r}\frac{\partial q_1}{\partial\vartheta} - \frac{q_2}{r} + \frac{\partial q_2}{\partial r}\right)$$

$$\tau_{r\varphi} = A_r\left(\frac{1}{r\sin\vartheta}\frac{\partial q_1}{\partial\varphi} - \frac{q_3}{r} + \frac{\partial q_3}{\partial r}\right) \qquad (3.13)$$

Since the depth of the ocean is much smaller than the radius of the earth, only the last term in each of the brackets in equation (3.13) is important. Expression (3.12) can then be written[1]

$$\frac{1}{\varrho}\left\{\frac{1}{r}\frac{\partial}{\partial\vartheta}\left(\tau_{r\varphi}\Big|_{h_b}^{h_s}\right) + \frac{\cot\vartheta}{r}\left(\tau_{r\varphi}\Big|_{h_b}^{h_s}\right) - \right.$$

$$- \frac{1}{r\sin\vartheta}\frac{\partial}{\partial\varphi}\left(\tau_{r\vartheta}\Big|_{h_b}^{h_s}\right) -$$

$$- \frac{1}{r}\left(\left[\frac{\partial}{\partial r}\left(A_r\frac{\partial q_3}{\partial r}\right)\right]\frac{\partial h}{\partial\vartheta}\right)\Big|_{h_b}^{h_s} +$$

$$\left. + \frac{1}{r\sin\vartheta}\left(\left[\frac{\partial}{\partial r}\left(A_r\frac{\partial q_2}{\partial r}\right)\right]\frac{\partial h}{\partial\varphi}\right)\Big|_{h_b}^{h_s}\right\} +$$

$$+ \frac{1}{\sin\vartheta}\int_{h_b}^{h_s}\frac{1}{r^2}\left[\frac{\partial}{\partial\vartheta}(r\sin\vartheta F_3^*) - \frac{\partial}{\partial\varphi}(rF_2^*)\right]dr \qquad (3.14)$$

where $\left([\ ]\frac{\partial h}{\partial\vartheta}\right)\Big|_{h_b}^{h_s}$ is an abbriviation for

$[\ ]_{r=h_s}\frac{\partial h_s}{\partial\vartheta} - [\ ]_{r=h_b}\frac{\partial h_b}{\partial\vartheta}$ and $\frac{\partial}{\partial\vartheta}\left(\tau_{r\varphi}\Big|_{h_b}^{h_s}\right) = \frac{\partial}{\partial\vartheta}[\tau_{r\varphi}(h_s, \vartheta, \varphi, t) - \tau_{r\varphi}(h_b, \vartheta, \varphi, t)]$.

[1] For details see: G. W. MORGAN; On the integration over depth of the equations for the wind-driven ocean circulation; Reference No. 54-89; unpublished manuscript of the Woods Hole Oceanographic Institution, December 1954.

Note that the three terms containing the shear stresses are approximately $\frac{1}{\varrho}(\text{curl}\,\boldsymbol{\tau})_1\Big|_{h_b}^{h_s}$, where $\boldsymbol{\tau}$ is the shear stress vector on the surfaces h_s or h_b. The additional surface terms arise from the fact that

$$\left(\frac{\partial}{\partial\vartheta}\frac{\partial q_3}{\partial r}\right)\Big|_{h_b}^{h_s} \neq \frac{\partial}{\partial\vartheta}\left[\left(\frac{\partial q_3}{\partial r}\right)\Big|_{h_b}^{h}\right]$$

4. Interior Equations

In this section we derive approximate equations applicable to the interior of the ocean, i.e. to a region sufficiently far removed from all shores. A more precise definition of the "interior region" will be given in Section 5. We assume, as do other investigators, that all terms which are nonlinear in the velocity components, as well as the contributions of lateral eddy viscosity are negligibly small there. It is further assumed that the pressure is hydrostatic everywhere in the ocean, i.e. that all terms involving velocity components in (3.1) are negligible. These assumptions can be readily justified by examining the orders of magnitude of the terms in the equations. Equation (3.1) becomes

$$\frac{\partial p}{\partial r} = \varrho g \tag{4.1}$$

Integration of equation (4.1) together with the boundary condition $p=0$ at $r=h_s$ gives

$$p = \varrho g\,(h_s - r). \tag{4.2}$$

For the two-layer model, we assume that all velocities are negligible in the lower layer so that the pressure gradients vanish there. This leads to the two relations

$$\frac{\partial h_b}{\partial\vartheta} = -\frac{\varrho}{\Delta\varrho}\frac{\partial h_s}{\partial\vartheta},\quad \frac{\partial h_b}{\partial\varphi} = -\frac{\varrho}{\Delta\varrho}\frac{\partial h_b}{\partial\varphi} \tag{4.3}$$

where $\Delta\varrho$ is the density difference between the two layers. Letting

$$D = h_s - h_b \tag{4.4}$$

we can write

$$\frac{\partial h_s}{\partial\vartheta} = \frac{\partial D}{\partial\vartheta},\quad \frac{\partial h_s}{\partial\varphi} = \frac{\partial D}{\partial\varphi} \tag{4.5}$$

for the homogeneous ocean (h_b having been assumed constant) and

$$\frac{\partial h_s}{\partial\vartheta} = \frac{\Delta\varrho}{\varrho}\frac{\partial D}{\partial\vartheta},\quad \frac{\partial h_s}{\partial\varphi} = \frac{\Delta\varrho}{\varrho}\frac{\partial D}{\partial\varphi} \tag{4.6}$$

for the two-layer model, where it has been assumed that $\Delta\varrho \ll \varrho$.

The momentum equations (3.2) and (3.3) become, using (3.11) and (4.2)

$$-2\Omega q_3\cos\vartheta = -g\frac{1}{r}\frac{\partial h_s}{\partial\vartheta} + \frac{1}{\varrho}\frac{1}{r^2}\frac{\partial}{\partial r}\left(A_r r^2\frac{\partial q_2}{\partial r}\right) \tag{4.7}$$

$$2\Omega q_2\cos\vartheta + 2\Omega q_1\sin\vartheta = -g\frac{1}{r\sin\vartheta}\frac{\partial h_s}{\partial\varphi} + \frac{1}{\varrho}\frac{1}{r^2}\frac{\partial}{\partial r}\left(A_r r^2\frac{\partial q_3}{\partial r}\right) \tag{4.8}$$

Before writing the approximate form of the vorticity equation (3.10) it is convenient to evaluate the term $(q_1 f)\Big|_{h_b}^{h_s}$. Applying the kinetic boundary conditions

$$\frac{D}{Dt}(h_s - r) = \frac{D}{Dt}(h_b - r) = 0 \tag{4.9}$$

we have

$$(q_1 f)\Big|_{h_b}^{h_s} = f\left(\frac{q_2}{r}\frac{\partial h}{\partial\vartheta} + \frac{q_3}{r\sin\vartheta}\frac{\partial h}{\partial\varphi}\right)\Big|_{h_b}^{h_s} \tag{4.10}$$

Evaluating the right side by means of equations (4.7) and (4.8), we have

$$(q_1 f)\Big|_{h_b}^{h_s} = -\left(\frac{2\Omega}{r}\sin\vartheta q_1\frac{\partial h}{\partial\vartheta}\right)\Big|_{h_b}^{h} + \frac{1}{\varrho}\left\{\left(\frac{1}{r^3}\frac{\partial}{\partial r}\left[A_r r^2\frac{\partial q_3}{\partial r}\right]\frac{\partial h}{\partial\vartheta}\right)\Big|_{h_b}^{h_s} - \left(\frac{1}{r^3\sin\vartheta}\frac{\partial}{\partial r}\left[A_r r^2\frac{\partial q_2}{\partial r}\right]\frac{\partial h}{\partial\varphi}\right)\Big|_{h_b}^{h_s}\right\} \tag{4.11}$$

When this expression is substituted into equation (3.10) the last two terms cancel the corresponding terms on the right side of equation (3.10) as given by expression (3.14), provided we neglect the variation of r in equation (4.11).

The resulting vorticity equation (without nonlinear and lateral eddy viscosity terms) may be simplified further by noting that the slopes of the top and bottom surfaces will be much less than one, so that $q_1 \ll q_2$. Thus, only the term in df/dt is important on the left side and, using (3.8), equation (3.10) becomes approximately

$$-\frac{2\Omega}{r}\sin\vartheta\int_{h_b}^{h_s} q_2 dr = \frac{1}{\varrho}\left\{\frac{1}{r}\frac{\partial}{\partial\vartheta}\left(\tau_{r\varphi}\Big|_{h_b}^{h_s}\right) + \right.$$

$$\left. + \frac{\cot\vartheta}{r}\left(\tau_{r\varphi}\Big|_{h_b}^{h_s}\right) - \frac{1}{r\sin\vartheta}\frac{\partial}{\partial\varphi}\left(\tau_{r\vartheta}\Big|_{h_b}^{h_s}\right)\right\} \quad (4.12)$$

Integration of the approximate momentum equations (4.7) and (4.8) leads to

$$-2\Omega\cos\vartheta\int_{h_b}^{h_s} q_3 dr = -g'\frac{1}{r}D\frac{\partial D}{\partial\vartheta} + \frac{1}{\varrho}(\tau_{r\vartheta})\Big|_{h_b}^{h_s} \quad (4.13)$$

$$2\Omega\cos\vartheta\int_{h_b}^{h_s} q_2 dr = -g'\frac{1}{r\sin\vartheta}D\frac{\partial D}{\partial\varphi} + \frac{1}{\varrho}(\tau_{r\varphi})\Big|_{h_b}^{h_s} \quad (4.14)$$

where we have used (4.4) to (4.6) and have neglected q_1, and

$$\left.\begin{aligned} g' &\equiv g && \text{in the homogeneous ocean} \\ g' &\equiv \frac{\Delta\varrho}{\varrho}g && \text{in the two-layer ocean} \end{aligned}\right\} \quad (4.15)$$

The integrated continuity equation is readily shown to be

$$\frac{\partial}{\partial\vartheta}\int_{h_b}^{h_s}\sin\vartheta q_2 dr + \frac{\partial}{\partial\varphi}\int_{h_b}^{h_s} q_3 dr = 0 \quad (4.16)$$

This relation is approximate in that the variation of r over the range of integration has been neglected. Introducing the "transport" components Q_2, Q_3, equation (4.16) is satisfied by defining the transport stream function ψ by the relations

$$\left.\begin{aligned} Q_2 &\equiv \int_{h_b}^{h_s} q_2 dr \equiv -\frac{1}{r\sin\vartheta}\frac{\partial\psi}{\partial\varphi} \\ Q_3 &\equiv \int_{h_b}^{h_s} q_3 dr \equiv -\frac{1}{r}\frac{\partial\psi}{\partial\vartheta} \end{aligned}\right\} \quad (4.17)$$

Equations (4.12) to (4.14) and (4.17) are the equations which we shall apply to the interior of the ocean.

5. Boundary Equations

a) Preliminary discussion.

To conform with reality, the circulation to be predicted by theory will have to exhibit relatively large velocities and velocity gradients at least near the western shore. Hence the approximations made in Section 4 for the interior region of the ocean cannot be expected to hold there. This is otherwise evident from a mathematical point of view since the approximate equations (4.12) to (4.16) do not constitute a system of a sufficiently high order to yield solutions which satisfy all boundary conditions. Hence these equations are not adequate for the entire enclosed ocean.

It has been assumed by other investigators (e.g. MUNK, 1950) that the influence of lateral eddy viscosity, while negligible in the interior, becomes important near the shore. The theory based on this assumption has led to a circulation pattern which looks remarkably realistic. As was already mentioned in the introduction, the theory has been criticized, however, because of the need for the empirical choice of the value of the coefficient of lateral eddy viscosity and the fact that the value which gives the proper width to the stream on the western shore is larger than one might expect from independent considerations. It is useful to consider the merits of this "viscous" theory from other points of view.

It was stated in the introduction that the torque due to the frictional forces on the shores has, at times, been held to be the torque which balances the torque applied by the wind. Now the viscous theory shows that the magnitude of the shore friction torque depends on the value of the viscosity (the shear stress on the shore being proportional to the viscosity and the normal derivative of the tangential velocity component, and the latter varying as viscosity to the minus two-thirds power). Hence, if the argument were correct, the value of the viscosity should be chosen so as to satisfy the torque balance! Fortunately the discussion in Section 2 relieves us of this requirement. If the friction torque is essential to the torque balance, it is certainly not the only contribution.

Consider now briefly, from a physical point of view, the role of the shore in producing an intense current. The solution of the interior vorticity and continuity equations (4.12) and (4.16) with a realistic wind distribution and neglecting bottom friction (see Section 6) leads to a southward transport component over the southern interior. The equations do not determine the direction of the other component. This evidently depends on the flow near the coast. Whichever it is, in a model which requires that the circulation be confined essentially to the northern hemisphere, the stipulation of an eastern or western shore must give rise to an intense northward current on one of the coasts, since the water which flows toward this coast has to be turned to the north to satisfy continuity. The stream will have to be narrow and hence intense if it is not to interfere with the concept of the interior region. Thus, the boundary condition of vanishing normal velocity on the shore is responsible for turning the current northward; the mechanism which accounts for the narrowness of this current (and which will determine on which of the two shores the current exists) remains to be investigated, but it appears reasonable that the usual viscous boundary condition of no slip will not have to play an essential role in the creation of the stream. This is also indicated by the viscous theory which shows that even if the extreme condition of zero normal derivative of the tangential transport is specified on the coast, the width and intensity of the stream are essentially unaffected. If, however, the no-slip condition is not essential, then the function of viscosity may not be paramount in the formation of the stream. It is only necessary to have a system of equations which is of sufficiently high order to be capable of yielding solutions which can satisfy the condition of vanishing normal transport. This, of course, can be accomplished by including the nonlinear inertia terms. The inclusion of viscosity, on the other hand, leads to a higher order system which requires another and, it seems, extraneous boundary condition.

It is important to note that the preceding discussion, having been restricted to the formative stage of the northward stream, does not necessarily suggest that lateral viscosity will not be important anywhere in the system. Since our study of the moment of momentum balance gave no conclusive answer to this question, it may be useful to examine it here from another point of view.

Imagine that the flow is contained between two solid concentric spheres and that it is created by the application of body forces uniformly distributed over the depth, rather than by surface forces. If there is no top or bottom friction we may expect the motion to be independent of r and to have vanishing radial velocity. The vorticity equation (3.6) then becomes

$$\frac{d}{dt}(\zeta_1 + f) = (\text{curl}\,\boldsymbol{B})_1 + \begin{matrix}\text{lateral eddy}\\ \text{viscosity terms}\end{matrix} \qquad (5.1)$$

where $\boldsymbol{B}$ represents the body forces. If $(\text{curl}\,\boldsymbol{B})_1$ is everywhere positive, (as we may expect $(\text{curl}\,\boldsymbol{\tau})_1\Big|^{h_s}$, the curl of the wind stress, to be), and if viscosity is absent, then equation (5.1) says that the quantity $\zeta_1 + f$ will always increase as we follow a particle. If the system is closed, this leads to a nonsteady flow. Hence, for steady flow, lateral friction must be important at least in some region through which every particle will have to pass.

This conclusion also follows immediately from energy considerations. The direction of the flow to be expected in the interior is such that the body force would do positive work on the system. In the absence of lateral eddy viscosity, however, there is no mechanism for dissipating the resulting increase in kinetic energy.

The author has so far not succeeded in carrying out an analogous examination of the variation of $\zeta_1 + f$ for the actual problem. It may be noted, however, that in our formulation the transfer of the wind stress to the water occurs by means of vertical eddy viscosity and that, therefore, a mechanism for energy dissipation exists even in the absence of lateral eddy viscosity. Thus, the energy argument breaks down.

b) A new model.

The considerations presented so far suggest that we adopt a new model for our system. Let us imagine the ocean between, say, 10° latitude and 50° latitude to consist of a southern and a northern portion with the dividing circle of latitude at about 35°. The southern portion is further divided as shown. The figure also shows a typical streamline of the anticipated circulation, most, or perhaps all, of the streamlines being expected to pass through all three regions.

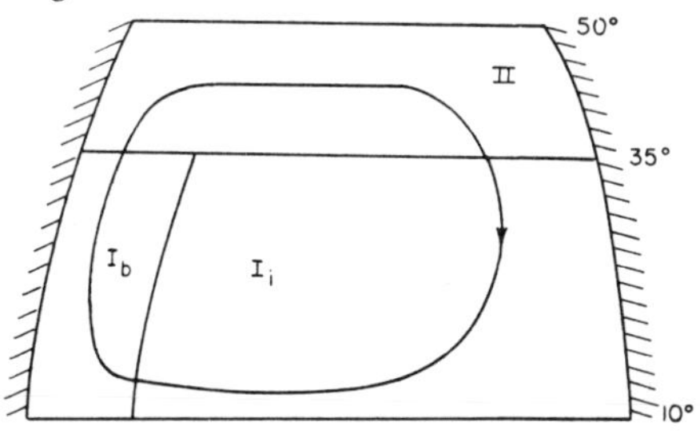

Fig. 1. The three regions of a new ocean model. I_i: interior region; I_b: frictionless stream region; II: northern region; nonsteady and lateral friction effects possibly important.

Our theory will apply to the interior region I_i and the boundary region I_b; (it will be seen that no boundary region is required on the eastern shore). In I_i the equations of Section 4 are applicable. In I_b nonlinear inertia, but not viscosity, will be included. In the Atlantic, I_b is to include the Gulf Stream north to about Cape Hatteras. In region II nonlinear, viscous and nonsteady effects may be important. This region includes the Gulf Stream meanders. If it turns out that lateral viscosity must be present somewhere in the system, its influence will be confined to region II. It is quite possible that the analysis of the problem in regions I and II together may have to include instability of the meanders, i.e. nonsteady effects. These, too, are assumed to be present in II only. The analysis of the flow in I is based on the assumption that this flow can be studied without inquiring into the conditions in II. Thus, whatever occurs in II, the flow which emerges from there into I_i is such that it obeys our interior equations. Similarly, the flow entering II from I_b is supposed to be determined by conditions in I_i and I_b alone.

c) Order of magnitude estimates.

The terms in the vorticity equation (3.10) may be grouped into three categories: (i) terms nonlinear in the velocities, (ii) terms due to the earth's rotation, (iii) terms resulting from eddy viscosity. The relative importance of each group will be examined in the following subsection by the usual procedures of boundary analysis. In the present section we carry out a preliminary simplification by comparing the relative magnitudes of the terms within each group.

(i) It will be assumed that the shores are given by two meridians. We must then expect that, in the boundary region, $|q_3| \ll |q_2|$ and derivatives parallel to the shore, $\left(\frac{\partial}{\partial\vartheta}\right)$, will be much smaller than those normal to the shore, $\left(\frac{\partial}{\partial\varphi}\right)$, Hence, from equation (3.5), $\zeta_1 \approx -(1/r \sin\vartheta)(\partial q_2/\partial\varphi)$. The magnitude of q_1 is readily estimated from the kinetic boundary condition, equation (4.9), in terms of q_2, q_3 and the slopes of h_s and h_b. For the homogeneous ocean q_1 is very small due to the small surface slope. For the two-layer ocean the principal contribution is due to the slope of h_b, the thermocline, the variation of h_b being of the order of the depth D itself.

Examining the third integral in equation (3.10), it is clear that the first, second and fourth terms are negligible compared with the third.

The contributions of $\int_{h_b}^{h_s} (d\zeta_1/dt)dr$ and $(q_1\zeta_1)\Big|_{h_b}^{h_s}$ are seen to be of equal importance in the two-layer case. To compare these terms with the remaining nonlinear terms involving radial differentiation, we must obtain an estimate of $\partial q_2/\partial r$. The second, third and fourth terms of equation (3.10) have the following orders of magnitude for a two-layer model:

$$[(q_1/r)(\partial q_2/\partial\varphi)]_{r=h_b}; \quad (q_1/r)_{r=h_b}\left[(\partial q_2/\partial\varphi)\Big|_{h_b}^{h_s}\right];$$
$$(\partial q_1/\partial\varphi)_{r=h_b}\left[(q_2/r)\Big|_{h_b}^{h_s}\right].$$

(For a homogeneous ocean q_1 is so small everywhere that all these terms are negligible.) The second and third of the above expressions involve a difference in the values at h_s and h_b of the quantities $\partial q_2/\partial\varphi$ and q_2, respectively. If these differences are of the order of the quantities themselves, then all terms must be expected to be of equal importance. We assume in the following that these differences are much smaller than the quantities themselves and hence that the term $(q_1 \zeta_1)\Big|_{h_b}^{h_s}$, predominates. This implies that the top and bottom shear stresses which constitute the principal cause of the radial variation of q_2 are relatively unimportant in the boundary region, thus leaving q_2 essentially uniform with depth. This condition can probably be relaxed somewhat because our estimates of the third and fourth terms are likely to be on the high side, q_1 and $\partial q_1/\partial\varphi$ having been taken out of the integrals and evaluated at $r = h_b$ where they will be greatest. Nevertheless it may be important to note that the justification for omitting the terms under consideration is not beyond question.

(ii) As in (i), the first two terms involving Ω in equation (3.10) are seen to be of the same order, while the third one is negligible.

(iii) We turn to expression (3.12) for the terms due to eddy viscosity. Of the three terms involving radial eddy viscosity the last one will predominate. The principal contribution due to lateral eddy viscosity comes from F_2^* and is approximately

$$\frac{1}{\varrho r^3 \sin^3\vartheta}\int_{h_b}^{h_s} A_L \frac{\partial^3 q_2}{\partial\varphi^3}\,dr$$

A_L denoting the lateral eddy viscosity.

The simplified vorticity equation (3.10) now becomes

$$\int_{h_b}^{h_s}\frac{d}{dt}(\zeta_1 + f)\,dr - [q_1(\zeta_1 + f)]\Big|_{h_b}^{h_s} =$$

$$= -\frac{1}{\varrho}\frac{1}{r}\left(A_r\frac{\partial^2 q_2}{\partial r\partial\varphi}\right)\Big|_{h_b}^{h_s} -$$

$$-\frac{1}{r^3\sin^3\vartheta}\int_{h_b}^{h_s} A_L\,\partial^2 q_2/\partial\varphi^2\cdot dr \qquad (5.2)$$

with $\zeta_1 \simeq -(1/r\sin\vartheta)\,(\partial q_2/\partial\varphi)$.

d) Boundary layer analysis.

In this subsection the technique of boundary layer analysis is employed to examine the relative magnitudes of the terms in (5.2). This technique assumes that a boundary layer type of solution exists. If it does, then the procedure readily yields an estimate of some of the properties of the solution; in this case, of the width and intensity of the stream.

We first assume that the essence of the phenomenon of interest to us will not be lost if we neglect the radial variation of the velocity components and of A_L within the boundary layer for the purpose of evaluating the integrals in equation (5.2). We also assume that the radial eddy viscosity term is not important. This assumption may not be valid for a homogeneous or a two-layer ocean, or perhaps even for a more realistic model, but an argument in its favor might be as follows. At the top surface the radial velocity gradient will be zero in the absence of a meridional wind. At the bottom surface the radial eddy viscosity may be sufficiently small to keep $(A_r\,\partial^2 q_2/\partial r\partial\varphi)_{r=h_b}$ small. We make the assumption in spite of the uncertainty of its validity because of the desirability of investigating the boundary solution in the complete absence of friction. Equation (5.2) becomes

$$D\frac{d(\zeta_1 + f)}{dt} - [q_1(\zeta_1 + f)]\Big|_{h_b}^{h_s} =$$

$$= -\frac{D}{\varrho r^3\sin^3\vartheta}A_L\frac{\partial^2 q_2}{\partial\varphi^2} \qquad (5.3)$$

or, using the kinetic boundary conditions (4.9),

$$\frac{d}{dt}\left(\frac{\zeta_1 + f}{D}\right) = -\frac{1}{D\varrho r^3\sin^3\vartheta}A_L\frac{\partial^3 q_2}{\partial\varphi^3} \qquad (5.4)$$

Equation (5.4) is rendered dimensionless by the following transformations

$$\left.\begin{array}{ll} q_2 = q^* q_2' & q_3 = q^* q_3' \\ \frac{1}{r}\frac{\partial}{\partial\vartheta} \approx \frac{1}{s}\frac{\partial}{\partial\vartheta'} & \frac{1}{r}\frac{\partial}{\partial\varphi} \approx \frac{1}{s}\frac{\partial}{\partial\varphi'} \\ \beta = \frac{2\,\Omega}{r} & \end{array}\right\} \qquad (5.5)$$

where q^* is a characteristic velocity taken to be a measure of the zonal velocity in the transition region from the interior to the boundary layer, s is the south-north extent of region I, and $\sin\vartheta$ is approximated by one. We further restrict ourselves for the moment to an homogeneous ocean or to a two-layer model with such a deep upper layer that the depth may be regarded as uniform. Equation (5.4) then becomes approximately

$$\frac{q^*}{s^2\beta}\left(q_2'\frac{\partial^2 q_2'}{\partial\vartheta'\partial\varphi'}+q_3'\frac{\partial^2 q_2'}{\partial\varphi'^2}-\cos\vartheta\, q_2'\frac{\partial q_2'}{\partial\varphi'}\right)+ + q_2' = \frac{A_L}{s^3\beta}\frac{\partial^3 q_2'}{\partial\varphi'^3} \qquad (5.6)$$

According to our discussion in Sections 5 a) and 5 b), we expect that the nonlinear terms will be important in the boundary layer. Since they are negligible in the interior, the parameter

$$N \equiv \frac{q^*}{s^2\beta} \qquad (5.7)$$

must be much less than one. Hence the terms cannot be important in the boundary layer unless the derivatives, and possibly the functions themselves, are large there. We therefore set

$$\varphi' = N^m\varphi'', \quad q_2' = N^{-n}q_2'' \qquad (5.8)$$

where m, n are to be determined and are expected to be positive. We hope to find a transformation (5.8) such that $q_2''(\vartheta_1'\varphi'')$, $q_3'(\vartheta',\varphi'')$ and their derivatives are of order one in the boundary layer. The magnitude of each term will then be indicated by its coefficient.

The continuity equation (4.16) shows that $m=n$ and equation (5.6) becomes

$$N^{1-3m}\left(q_2''\frac{\partial^2 q_2''}{\partial\vartheta'\partial\varphi''}+q_3'\frac{\partial^2 q_2''}{\partial\varphi''^2}-\cos\vartheta\, q_2''\frac{\partial q_2''}{\partial\varphi''}\right)+ + N^{-m}q_2'' = N^{-4m}\frac{A_L}{\varrho s^3\beta}\frac{\partial^3 q_2''}{\partial\varphi''^3} \qquad (5.9)$$

Since we expect nonlinear and Coriolis terms to balance, we must have $m=\frac{1}{2}$. The terms due to lateral eddy viscosity will be unimportant if $N^{-3/2}A_L/\varrho s^3\beta = \beta^{1/2}A_L/\varrho q^{*3/2} \ll 1$. The width of the stream will be of order $sN^{1/2} = (q^*/\beta)^{1/2}$, and the meridional velocity component will be of order $q^*N^{-1/2} = s(q^*\beta)^{1/2}$. With $\beta = 2\times10^{-13}\cdot(\text{cm sec})^{-1}$, $q^x = 10$ cm sec^{-1} this gives approximately 70 km for the width of the stream, which is the correct order of magnitude. The condition for smallness of the friction terms places an upper bound of approximately 5×10^6 cm^2 sec^{-1} on the magnitude of A_L. Assuming that this corresponds to actual conditions and that, therefore, lateral eddy viscosity is negligible, the vorticity equation (5.4) becomes

$$\frac{d}{dt}\left(\frac{\zeta_1+f}{D}\right) = 0 \qquad (5.10)$$

Since, in this equation, the variation of ζ_1, q_2, q_3 with depth has, effectively, been neglected, the derivative d/dt may be interpreted as the rate of change as one follows a vertical column of water in its horizontal motion, and the equation (5.10) states that the potential vorticity associated with such a column is conserved during its motion in the boundary region. Using equation (4.17), equation (5.10) can be integrated along a "transport line", i.e. a line of constant ψ, to give

$$\frac{\zeta_1+f}{D} = F(\psi) \qquad (5.11)$$

where F is a function which must be determined by matching the distribution of $(\zeta_1+f)/D$ in the boundary with the distribution in the interior near the edge of the boundary layer.

e) The momentum equations in the boundary layer.

The considerations contained in the preceding sections may now be applied to the integrals over depth of the momentum equations (3.2) and (3.3) to derive approximate equations which are consistent with the assumptions made in deriving the vorticity equation. They are

$$\int_{h_b}^{h_s}\left(\frac{q_2}{r}\frac{\partial q_2}{\partial\vartheta}+\frac{q_3}{r\sin\vartheta}\frac{\partial q_2}{\partial\varphi}\right)dr - 2\Omega\cos\vartheta\int_{h_b}^{h_s} q_3\,dr = = -g'\frac{1}{r}D\frac{\partial D}{\partial\vartheta} \qquad (5.12)$$

$$2\Omega\cos\vartheta\int_{h_b}^{h} q_2\,dr = -g'\frac{1}{r\sin\vartheta}D\frac{\partial D}{\partial\varphi} \qquad (5.13)$$

We note that the meridional transport component is geostrophic, but that the zonal component is not, the nonlinear terms being as important as the Coriolis contribution.

Neglecting the variation of the integrands with depth, we derive an approximate Bernoulli equation by multiplying equation (5.12) by q_2, equation (5.13) by q_3, adding the resulting equations to obtain

$$\frac{d}{dt}\left(\frac{q_2^2}{2}\right)+g'\frac{dD}{dt}=0, \qquad (5.14)$$

and finally integrating along a streamline (or transport line), giving

$$\frac{q_2^2}{2}+g'D=B(\psi) \qquad (5.15)$$

where B is an arbitrary function which must be determined by matching the boundary with the interior solution.

6. Transformation to Surface Coordinates

Having derived the equations in terms of spherical coordinates in an effort not to lose any important effects of the spherical ocean shape by premature introduction of plane coordinates, we are now ready to make this transformation to give the equations a more familiar appearance.

Our boundary layer analysis has been based on the assumption that the derivative $\partial/\partial\varphi$ represents differentiation normal to the coast. Hence two meridians are taken to represent the coast lines. The simplest coordinate system will then be one in which these are coordinate lines. Hence, set

$$\left.\begin{array}{lll} x=R\varphi, & y=R(K-\vartheta) & z=r-R \\ u=q_3, & v=-q_2 & \\ U=Q_3, & V=-Q_2 & \\ \tau_x=\tau_{r\varphi}, & \tau_y=-\tau_{r\vartheta} & \end{array}\right\} \qquad (6.1)$$

where K is the colatitude of the southern boundary of region I, R is the radius of the undisturbed ocean surface. Note that while y measures distance along a meridian of a sphere of radius R, x does not measure exact distance along a circle of latitude. We have

$$\frac{\partial}{\partial r}=\frac{\partial}{\partial z};\quad \frac{\partial}{\partial\vartheta}=-R\frac{\partial}{\partial y};\quad \frac{\partial}{\partial\varphi}=R\frac{\partial}{\partial x} \qquad (6.2)$$

If, instead of x, an alternative coordinate x' which does measure distance along a circle of latitude were chosen, (e.g. $x'=\varphi R\sin\vartheta$), then the most convenient geometrical shape in the x'—y plane, the rectangle, would represent a less realistic configuration than does the rectangle in the x—y plane which corresponds to an ocean whose east and west shores are meridians. Moreover, the velocity component v would then be an inconvenient variable since it would not represent the velocity in the direction of the constant x' curves.[1]

The interior equations (4.12), (4.13), (4.14), (4.17) become

$$\beta\sin\vartheta\int_{h_b-R}^{h_s-R} v\,dz=$$

$$=\frac{1}{\varrho}\left(-\frac{\partial\tau_x}{\partial y}+\frac{\cot\vartheta}{R}\tau_x+\frac{1}{\sin\vartheta}\frac{\partial\tau_y}{\partial x}\right)_{z=h_b-R} \qquad (6.3)$$

$$2\Omega\cos\vartheta\int_{h_b-R}^{h_s-R} u\,dz=-\frac{g'}{2}\frac{\partial D^2}{\partial y}+\frac{1}{\varrho}(\tau_y)_{z=h_s-R} \qquad (6.4)$$

$$-2\Omega\cos\vartheta\int_{h_b-R}^{h_s-R} v\,dz=-$$

$$-\frac{g'}{2\sin\vartheta}\frac{\partial D^2}{\partial x}+\frac{1}{\varrho}(\tau_x)_{z=h_s-R} \qquad (6.5)$$

$$V=\int_{h_b-R}^{h_s-R} v\,dz=\frac{1}{\sin\vartheta}\frac{\partial\psi}{\partial x},\quad U=\int_{h_b-R}^{h_s-R} u\,dz=-\frac{\partial\psi}{\partial y} \qquad (6.6)$$

[1] The reader may wish to contrast our system with that of MUNK 1950 and MUNK-CARRIER 1950 whose x coordinate measures distance, with the result that the rectangle in the x—y plane does not correspond to a realistic ocean shape. This leads Munk-Carrier to consider a triangle. The rectangle in our x—y plane is perhaps an equally good approximation to the real ocean shape.

The agreement of corresponding terms in Munk's equations and in ours is not complete. This is due to the fact that Munk's equations have apparently not been derived by a systematic transformation of variables and coordinates from a spherical system; hence there is some question concerning the relation of Munk's variables to those in the actual spherical system.

where we have approximated $1/r$ by $1/R$ and, consistent with the assumption already made in the derivation of the boundary equations, have neglected the shear stress at the bottom surface $z = h_b - R$.

The boundary equations (5.11), (5.12), (5.13), (5.15) become

$$\frac{\dfrac{1}{\sin\vartheta}\dfrac{\partial v}{\partial x} + 2\Omega\cos\vartheta}{D} = F(\psi) \qquad (6.7)$$

$$\int_{h_b-R}^{h_s-R}\left(v\frac{\partial v}{\partial y} + \frac{u}{\sin\vartheta}\frac{\partial v}{\partial x}\right)dz + 2\Omega\cos\vartheta\int_{h_b-R}^{h_s-R} u\,dz = -\frac{g'}{2}\frac{\partial D^2}{\partial y} \qquad (6.8)$$

$$-2\Omega\cos\vartheta\int_{h_b-R}^{h_s-R} v\,dz = -\frac{g'}{2\sin\vartheta}\frac{\partial D^2}{\partial x} \qquad (6.9)$$

$$\frac{v^2}{2} + g'D = B(\psi) \qquad (6.10)$$

Just as in the derivation of the vorticity equation (6.7), the integrals appearing in equations (6.8) to (6.9) will be evaluated approximately by neglecting the z variation of the integrands.

7. The homogeneous Ocean with simple Wind Distribution

The homogeneous model is important principally because of the insight that will be gained into the role of density stratification in the formation of the western stream by comparing the behaviour of this model with that of a two-layer ocean. The most important question to be investigated in this connection is whether either the variation of the Coriolis parameter with latitude, or the density stratification, or both, are indispensable. Because of its simplicity, the homogeneous model also readily affords insight into the entire phenomenon of the coastal stream.

Assume the wind stresses

$$\tau_x = -W\left(1 - \frac{y^2}{s^2}\right), \quad \tau_y = 0, \quad 0 \le y \le s \qquad (7.1)$$

s being the south-north extent of region I and W being a constant. Equation (6.3) becomes

$$\beta\sin\vartheta V_i = \frac{W}{\varrho}\left[-\frac{2y}{s^2} + \frac{\cot\vartheta}{R}\left(1 - \frac{y^2}{s^2}\right)\right] \qquad (7.2)$$

where the subscript i is used to denote quantities in the interior region I_i. For $\vartheta \ge 55°$ and $K = 75°$, $\cot\vartheta \le .7$ and $s \approx .35\ R$, so that the second term due to the curl of the wind is considerably smaller than the first term over most of the range. Accordingly, we neglect it. Using equation (6.6)

$$\frac{\partial\psi_i}{\partial x} = -\frac{2yW}{\varrho\beta s^2} \qquad (7.3)$$

$$\psi_i = -\frac{2yW}{\varrho\beta s^2}[x + l(y)] \qquad (7.4)$$

$$U_i = \frac{2W}{\varrho\beta s^2}(x + l) + \frac{2yW}{\varrho\beta s^2}\frac{dl}{dy} \qquad (7.5)$$

where $l(y)$ is an arbitrary function. Since we do not expect a strong current on the eastern coast, (the impossibility of such a current will shortly be demonstrated), we anticipate that the interior solution will be valid all the way to this coast. Hence, we want $U = 0$ at $x = a$, $x = 0$ and $x = a$ denoting the western and eastern shores. Thus in the region I_i

$$\psi_i = \frac{2yW}{\varrho\beta s^2}(a - x) \qquad (7.6)$$

$$U_i = -\frac{2W}{\varrho\beta s^2}(a - x) \qquad (7.7)$$

We now examine the boundary equations. From equations (6.6) and (6.7) and neglecting the radial variation of v,

$$\frac{\dfrac{1}{\sin^2\vartheta}\dfrac{\partial}{\partial x}\left(\dfrac{1}{D}\dfrac{\partial\psi}{\partial x}\right) + 2\Omega\cos\vartheta}{D} = F(\psi). \qquad (7.8)$$

Since $g' = g$ in the homogeneous case, it is clear from equations (6.8) and (6.9) that the surface slopes will be very small and that, for a reasonable average depth, the depth will be essentially uniform. Expanding $\cos\vartheta$ in a power series about $\vartheta = K$ and retaining the first two terms

$$2\Omega\cos\vartheta \approx 2\Omega\cos K + 2\Omega\frac{y}{R}\sin K \qquad (7.9)$$

or

$$f \approx f_K + \beta_K y, \quad \beta_K \equiv \frac{2\Omega}{R}\sin K, \quad f_K \equiv 2\Omega\cos K \qquad (7.10)$$

and equation (7.8) becomes

$$\frac{1}{\sin^2 \vartheta} \frac{1}{D} \frac{\partial^2 \psi}{\partial x^2} + f_K + \beta_K y = G(\psi) \qquad (7.11)$$

where $G(\psi) = DF(\psi)$, D being regarded constant.

According to boundary layer analysis, as discussed in Section 5, the $\partial/\partial x$ derivatives are large only in the boundary layer and decrease as one approaches the interior. The transition from boundary to interior regions is, of course, continuous, but, to simplify the terminology, let us define some suitable distance $x = L$ as the "edge" of the boundary layer, L being large enough so that the boundary layer solution there is essentially equal to the interior solution in the same neighborhood. We then have

$$f_K + \beta_K y = G(\psi_i) \text{ at } x = L \qquad (7.12)$$

But, from equation (7.6),

$$\psi_i(L, y) \approx \frac{2\,Wa}{\varrho \beta s^2} y \equiv U^* y \qquad (7.13)$$

since we expect $L \ll a$, and where U^* denotes the zonal transport into the boundary layer. Hence

$$f_K + \beta_K y = G(U^* y) \qquad (7.14)$$

and

$$G(\psi) = f_K + \frac{\beta_K}{U^*} \psi \qquad (7.15)$$

Substitution into equation (7.11) yields

$$\frac{\partial^2 \psi}{\partial x^2} - \frac{\sin^2\left(K - \frac{y}{R}\right) D\beta_K}{U^*} \psi = = -\sin^2\left(K - \frac{y}{R}\right) D\beta_K y \qquad (7.16)$$

If we consider a closed ocean basin, the coast $x = 0$ and the southern boundary $y = 0$ form a continuous transport line so that $\psi(0, y) = 0$. This boundary condition together with the matching condition as the interior is approached (equation 7.13) determine the constants of integration. The solution is

$$\psi = U^* y \left[1 - e^{-\left(\frac{\sin^2 (K - y/R)\, D\beta_K}{U^*}\right)^{1/2} x}\right] \qquad (7.17)$$

and, from equation (6.6)

$$V = (U^* D\beta_K)^{1/2} y e^{-\left(\frac{\sin^2 (K - y/R)\, D\beta_K}{U^*}\right)^{1/2} x} \qquad (7.18)$$

Thus the theory predicts an intense northward stream on the western coast, the width of the stream being given by, say,

$$\sin\left(K - \frac{y}{R}\right) \cdot L \approx 4 \left(\frac{u^*}{\beta_K}\right)^{1/2}$$

and the intensity of the northward velocity being of order $s(u^* \beta_K)^{1/2}$, where $u^* = U^*/D$. These results are seen to agree with the orders of magnitude previously derived directly from boundary analysis considerations in Section 5 d). Expressions (7.17), (7.18) are simpler and more revealing if we set

$$x \sin\left(K - \frac{y}{R}\right) = X \qquad (7.19)$$

X measuring true distance along a circle of latitude.

Curves 1 a of Figures 2 and 3 show the variation of ψ/Us and V/U^* with dimensionless distance X/s from the western shore at $y = s$ for values of U^* (10^5 cm^2 sec^{-1}) and s (2×10^8 cms) corresponding to the North Atlantic and for a depth D (or D^* in the terminology of Section 8) of 4×10^5 cms which corresponds to the total depth of the ocean. Hence the graphs may be interpreted as representing the Gulf Stream which would exist if the motion were barotropic. The stream is quite narrow (its width is about 40 km); the transport is very large near the coast and decreases very rapidly as the distance from the coast increases. The predicted flow is seen to exhibit what might be regarded as the principal qualitative property of the observed circulation—a westward interior transport being turned into a narrow, intense stream near the western coast—and the width of this stream has the appropriate order of magnitude.

The results obtained may be given a very simple physical interpretation. The vorticity equation (6.7), for D essentially constant, states that the absolute vorticity of a particle, $\zeta_1 + f$, is conserved. Since f increases as the particle travels northward, ζ_1 must decrease, and since ζ_1 $\left(\text{or } \frac{\partial v}{\partial X}\right)$ is approximately zero when the particle enters the boundary region it must become negative. Particles which approach the coast at low latitude, i.e. with small f, must undergo a large increase in f to reach a certain more northerly latitude, and hence acquire a large negative value of ζ_1 (or $\partial v/\partial X$). Those approaching with larger f need not suffer such a great change in f to reach the same northerly latitude and hence acquire less negative $\partial v/\partial X$. This gives rise to the exponential type of decline in current intensity from the coast to the interior.

It is now clear that the interior transport approaching the west coast could equally well be turned into an intense southward current if we did not stipulate that $y=0$ be a streamline in the boundary region, i.e. that the circulation be enclosed on the south. Following the same physical reasoning as before, a southward current means a decrease in f and hence positive $\partial v/\partial X$ to conserve vorticity. Further, the particles approaching the coast with larger f must acquire larger positive $\partial v/\partial X$ than must those approaching with smaller f. Hence we obtain a boundary layer solution with v having its greatest negative value at the coast and increasing to zero as the interior is approached.

Any flow pattern intermediate between the two already discussed, with a portion of the westward interior current being turned into an intense northward stream and the balance into an intense southward stream is also possible. The entire infinite family of solutions is obtained by stipulating the boundary condition

$$\psi(0, y) = \gamma s U^*, \quad 0 \le \gamma \le 1. \qquad (7.20)$$

This gives

$$\psi = U^* (\gamma s - y)\, e^{-\left(\frac{D\beta_K}{U^*}\right)^{1/2} X} + U^* y \qquad (7.21)$$

$$V = -(U^* D\beta_K)^{1/2} (\gamma s - y)\, e^{-\left(\frac{D\beta_K}{U^*}\right)^{1/2} X} \qquad (7.22)$$

Thus all particles approaching the boundary region north of $y=\gamma s$ (but, of course, south of $y=s$ to remain within region I) turn northward, those approaching between $y=0$ and $y=\gamma s$ turn southward, the transport line $\psi=U^*\gamma s$ dividing at $x=0$ to form the shoreline both south and north of $y=\gamma s$.

Which of all these solutions is the appropriate one depends on the appropriate choice of the boundary condition and this in turn is governed by considerations of mass conservation in the overall system.

Other solutions may be obtained, for example, by giving $\psi(0, y)$ a negative value. This gives a northward stream consisting not only of the water approaching the coast from the interior and being turned north, but also of water introduced into the stream in the boundary region across $y=0$, this extra flow preventing the transport line $\psi=0$ from reaching the coast.

Another important result which is evident immediately on physical grounds is that the factors which create an intense stream on the west coast could not create a similar stream on the east coast. To show this, let us suppose that the zonal transport component in the interior is eastward. If this transport is to turn northward, f must increase along a transport line, hence $\partial v/\partial X$ must become negative. Further, particles approaching with smaller f must acquire larger negative $\partial v/\partial X$, than those approaching with greater f. Hence the solution would require positive v, negative $\partial v/\partial X$, and v tending to zero as one leaves the boundary region and approaches the interior region. Obviously, these are incompatible conditions. A similar argument rules out a southward stream. Thus we see that a boundary layer type solution is possible in region I if the zonal transport is westward, but not if the zonal transport is eastward.

Mathematically, this is seen as follows. Since ψ_i is zero on $y=0$, and since $U_i = -\partial\psi_i/\partial y > 0$ for an eastward interior current, ψ_i would be negative for $y>0$; in particular ψ_i would be negative at the edge of the intense stream on the east coast. The matching with the boundary layer solution, analogous to equation (7.12), would then lead to an expression for $G(\psi)$ analogous to (7.15) with a minus sign in front of the term containing ψ. This gives rise to a plus sign for the ψ term in the equation analogous to (7.16) for the boundary layer stream function, and hence to trigonometric instead of exponential solutions. Hence no boundary layer type solution is possible.

To avoid confusion, it should be emphasized that the above conclusion does not in any way conflict with the well known problem of ideal, irrotational fluid theory, in which a flow impinges on a solid boundary placed normal to the undisturbed flow at infinity. This flow is not of the boundary layer type and the tangential current is just as wide and no more intense than the normal current. This type of flow was excluded from our investigations as soon as we made approximations appropriate to boundary layer type solutions.

It appears that the simple homogeneous ocean model contains the essential features of the type of circulation one expects. In the following section we investigate to what extent the two-layer model alters the phenomenon.

8. The Two-Layer Ocean with Simple Wind Distribution[1]

We consider the same problem as in Section 7 and make the same approximations except that now the variation of the depth D is taken into account. The interior relations (7.3) to (7.7) remain unchanged. We shall require a relation between U^x and D_i at the edge of the boundary layer. From equations (6.4) and (7.7), and setting $2\Omega \cos \vartheta = f \approx f_K + \beta_K y$, we have

$$D_i^2 = \left(f_K y + \frac{\beta_K y^2}{2}\right) \frac{4W}{\varrho \beta s^2 g'} (a - x) + C(x) \tag{8.1 a}$$

where $C(x)$ is still arbitrary. If D^* is the depth at $y = 0$ and at the edge of the boundary layer $x = L$, then $C(L) = D^{*2}$ and

$$D_i^2 (L, y) = \frac{2 U^x}{g'} \left(f_K y + \frac{\beta_K y^2}{2}\right) + D^{*2} \tag{8.1b}$$

Another expression for $D_i^2 (x, y)$ may be derived by using the momentum equation (6.5). It is approximately

$$D_i^2 = -\left(f_K y + \frac{\beta_K y^2}{2}\right) \frac{4W}{\varrho \beta s^2 g'} x - \frac{2 W \sin K}{\varrho g'} x + + C_1 (y) \tag{8.1 c}$$

Comparison with equation (8.1 a) yields

$$C(x) = D_a^2 + \frac{2 W \sin K}{\varrho g'} (a - x) \tag{8.2}$$

where D_a is a constant and denotes $D_i (a, y)$.

Instead of using the vorticity equation (6.7) it is more convenient, in the two-layer case, to use the momentum equation (6.9) and the Bernoulli equation (6.10). From equations (6.9) and (6.6)

$$\psi = \frac{g'}{2f} D^2 + C_3 (y) \tag{8.3}$$

where $C_3(y)$ is arbitrary and is determined by matching ψ and D with the interior solutions. We have from equations (7.13), (8.1) and (8.3)

$$U^* y = \frac{g'}{2f} \left[\frac{2 U^*}{g'} \left(f_K y + \frac{\beta_K y^2}{2}\right) + D^{*2}\right] + C_3 \tag{8.4}$$

whence

$$C_3 (y) = \frac{\beta_K y^2 U^*}{2f} - \frac{g' D^{*2}}{2f} \tag{8.5}$$

Substituting in equation (8.3) and solving for D^2 we obtain

$$D^2 = D^{*2} + \frac{2f}{g'} \psi - \frac{\beta_K y^2 U^*}{g'} \tag{8.6}$$

Equation (8.6) provides one relation between the unknowns ψ and D. A second relation is obtained from the Bernoulli equation (6.10). The unknown function $B(\psi)$ is again determined by matching with the interior solution. As one leaves the boundary region, equation (6.10) becomes

$$g' \left[D^{*2} + \frac{2 U^*}{g'} \left(f_K y + \frac{\beta_K y^2}{2}\right)\right]^{1/2} = B (U^* y) \tag{8.7}$$

[1] Some weeks following the final preparation of this paper Dr. J. G. Charney (1955) published a theory of the Gulf Stream much like the one contained in the following section. Charney's aim is to study a two-layer model which is fashioned to fit as closely as possible the observed topography of the thermocline between the Florida Straits and Cape Hatteras and the observed volume transports in the Stream, in order to determine how closely the theory can reproduce the observed flow. By contrast, this author's primary goal has been to critically analyze some of the questions connected with the formulation of a suitable theory and the development of the pertinent equations, and to investigate the mechanism which gives rise to the intense coastal current. This is done with a view to clarifying such problems as the roles of density stratification and the variation of the Coriolis parameter, the possibility of the existence of a current on the eastern boundary, the direction of the intense current, etc. In order not to obscure any of these aspects of the problem the simple model used to study the homogeneous ocean is retained in this section, where our theory is applied to the two-layer system, and no attempt is made to fit the model more closely to the Gulf Stream.

giving

$$B(\psi) = g'\left[D^{*2} + \frac{2f_K}{g'}\psi + \frac{\beta_K}{g'U^*}\psi^2\right]^{1/2} \quad (8.8)$$

Substitution into equation (6.10) yields

$$\frac{v^2}{2} = g'\left\{\left[D^{*2} + \frac{2f_K}{g'}\psi + \frac{\beta_K}{g'U^*}\psi^2\right]^{1/2} - D\right\} \quad (8.9)$$

Finally, replacing v by $(1/D \sin\vartheta)\, \partial\psi/\partial x$ from equation (6.6) and eliminating D by using equation (8.6), the following equation for ψ is obtained:

$$\left(\frac{\partial\psi}{\partial x}\right)^2 = 2g' \sin^2\left(K - \frac{y}{R}\right)\left[D^{*2} + \frac{2f}{g'}\psi - \frac{\beta_K y^2 U^*}{g'}\right] \left\{\left[D^{*2} + \frac{2f_K}{g'}\psi + \frac{\beta_K}{g'U^*}\psi^2\right]^{1/2} - \left[D^{*2} + \frac{2f}{g'}\psi - \frac{\beta_K y^2 U^*}{g'}\right]^{1/2}\right\} \quad (8.10)$$

The appropriate boundary condition is that $x=0$ be a streamline. As in Section 7 the particular value to be chosen for $\psi(0, y)$ depends on continuity considerations for the entire system. We shall restrict our numerical solutions to the model discussed in Section 7, i.e. to the case where the circulation is confined to a region north of $y=0$, so that

$$\psi(0, y) = 0 \quad (8.11)$$

We first note the very important result $\partial\psi/\partial x = 0$ for all x if $\beta_K = 0$. Thus, if the variation of the Coriolis parameter with latitude were neglected, no boundary stream could be produced. From a different point of view, the result shows that the variation in depth alone and its effect on the potential vorticity (equation (6.7)) cannot give rise to an intense stream. Thus, in the two-layer ocean, as in the homogeneous model, the variation of f is the essential phenomenon and it remains to investigate how the resulting flow pattern is modified by density stratification. More physical insight into this conclusion can perhaps be gained by the following consideration. Consider the change of relative vorticity ζ_1 $\left(\text{or } \frac{1}{\sin\vartheta}\frac{\partial v}{\partial x}\right)$ as one follows a streamline. Since, according to equation (6.7), potential vorticity is conserved, a change in ζ_1 will be due either to a change in f or to a change in D. We see from equation (8.6), however, that a change of D along a given streamline is due solely to a change in f. Hence, if f is constant, ζ_1 is constant along each streamline and since it is approximately zero near the edge of the boundary layer it must be zero everywhere. Thus the existence of β_K is the primary cause of the phenomenon. Inasmuch as β_K together with the small value of g' in the two-layer model give rise to a considerable change of depth along a streamline, and this change in turn effects the potential vorticity and hence the current, the latter is actually dependent on the depth (and hence on the density stratification) as well as on β_K.

Proceeding now with the analysis of the differential equation (8.10), we replace x by X according to equation (7.19) and then introduce the non-dimensional quantities X, $\bar{y}$, $\bar{\psi}$ by the relations

$$X = s\bar{X}, \quad y = s\bar{y}, \quad \psi = U^* s\bar{\psi}$$

so that $\bar{\psi}$ approaches $\bar{y}$ as one approaches the interior. Equation (8.10) becomes

$$\left(\frac{\partial\bar{\psi}}{\partial\bar{X}}\right)^2 = \frac{2\beta_K{}^{3/2}s^3}{U^{*1/2}g'^{1/2}}[\varepsilon + \delta\bar{\psi} + 2\bar{y}\bar{\psi} - \bar{y}^2] \{[\varepsilon + \delta\bar{\psi} + \bar{\psi}^2]^{1/2} - [\varepsilon + \delta\bar{\psi} + 2\bar{y}\bar{\psi} - \bar{y}^2]^{1/2}\} \quad (8.13)$$

where

$$\varepsilon = \frac{D^{*2}g'}{U^*\beta_K s^2} = \frac{D^* g'}{u^*\beta_K s^2}, \quad \delta = \frac{2f_K}{\beta_K s} \quad (8.14)$$

Introducing the transformation

$$\xi = \left(\frac{\beta_K{}^{3/2}s^3}{U^{*1/2}g'^{1/2}}\right)^{1/2}\bar{X}, \quad (8.15)$$

equation (8.13) becomes

$$\left(\frac{\partial\bar{\psi}}{\partial\xi}\right)^2 = 2[\varepsilon + \delta\bar{\psi} + 2\bar{y}\bar{\psi} - \bar{y}^2] \{[\varepsilon + \delta\bar{\psi} + \bar{\psi}^2]^{1/2} - [\varepsilon + \delta\bar{\psi} + 2\bar{y}\bar{\psi} - \bar{y}^2]^{1/2}\} \quad (8.16)$$

In this form all the parameters of the problem appear in the two dimensionless groupings ε and δ only. The meaning of δ is evident. The significance of ε is readily seen from equation (8.6). In terms of the dimensionless variables we have

$$D^2 = D^{*2} + \frac{2\,(f_K + \beta_K s\bar{y})}{g'}\,U^* s\bar{\psi} - \frac{U^*\beta_K s^2 \bar{y}^2}{g'} \qquad (8.17)$$

Thus $U^*\,\beta_K s^2/g'$ is a measure of the change of the square of the depth along a streamline and $\varepsilon^{1/2}$ is the ratio of the characteristic depth D^* to the characteristic change of depth.

In Section 7 the equations were applied to the homogeneous ocean by neglecting the variation in depth. Hence, it is to be expected that equation (8.16) will yield the solution for the homogeneous ocean when $\varepsilon \gg 1$; i.e. as far as the boundary region is concerned, a two-layer model, the depth of whose upper layer is very great compared to the change of that depth, behaves like a homogeneous model. The approximate analytical solution for $\varepsilon \gg 1$ is obtained in the following manner. The first bracket on the right-hand side of equation (8.16) is approximated by ε. The expressions inside each of the other brackets are divided by ε and the brackets expanded in binomial series retaining terms of order ε^{-1}. This yields

$$\left(\frac{\partial\bar{\psi}}{\partial\xi}\right)^2 \approx \varepsilon^{1/2}(\bar{y} - \bar{\psi})^2 \qquad (8.18)$$

Imposing the boundary condition $\bar{\psi}\,(0, \bar{y}) = 0$, the solution of equation (8.18) is

$$\bar{\psi} = \bar{y}(1 - e^{-1/4\,\xi}) \qquad (8.19)$$

which becomes identical with the solution obtained previously (equation 7.17) upon transformation to the appropriate variables.

If we deal with a homogeneous ocean, ε will in general be large because $g' = g$ and this quantity is of the order of 500 times as great as g' in a usual two-layer model. If we deal wthi a two-layer model ε may be made large by making D^* large. The preceding analysis

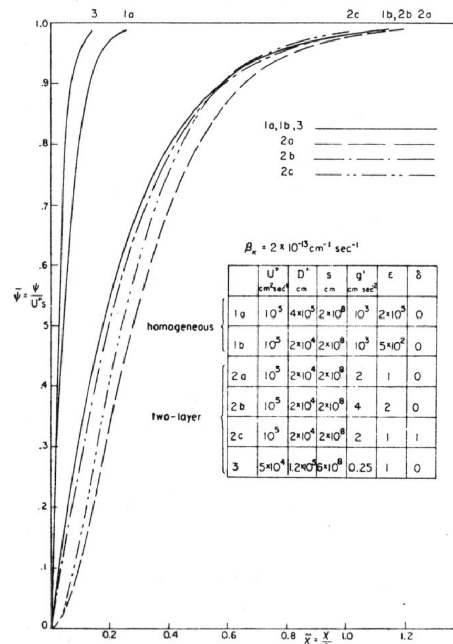

	U* cm²sec⁻¹	D* cm	s cm	g' cm sec⁻²	ε	δ
1a	10^5	4×10^5	2×10^8	10^3	2×10^5	0
1b	10^5	2×10^4	2×10^8	10^3	5×10^2	0
2a	10^5	2×10^4	2×10^8	2	1	0
2b	10^5	2×10^4	2×10^8	4	2	0
2c	10^5	2×10^4	2×10^8	2	1	1
3	5×10^4	1.2×10^5	6×10^8	0.25	1	0

Fig. 2. Dimensionless transport function $\bar{\psi}$ vs. dimensionless distance from western coast at northern boundary of region I_b for various values of the pertinent paramaters.

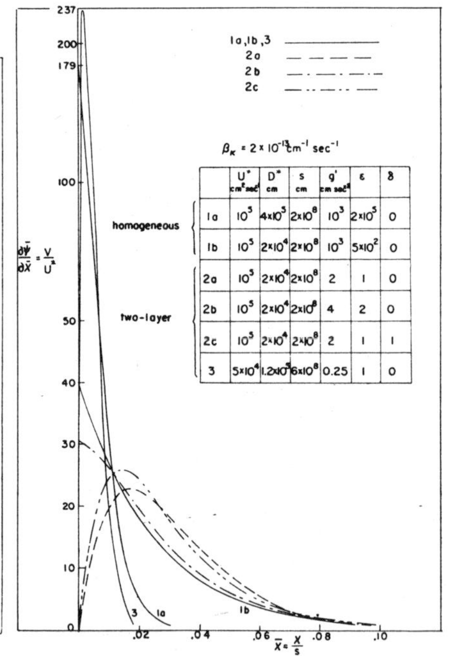

	U* cm²sec⁻¹	D* cm	s cm	g' cm sec⁻²	ε	δ
1a	10^5	4×10^5	2×10^8	10^3	2×10^5	0
1b	10^5	2×10^4	2×10^8	10^3	5×10^2	0
2a	10^5	2×10^4	2×10^8	2	1	0
2b	10^5	2×10^4	2×10^8	4	2	0
2c	10^5	2×10^4	2×10^8	2	1	1
3	5×10^4	1.2×10^5	6×10^8	0.25	1	0

Fig. 3. Dimensionless northward transport vs. dimensionless distance from western coast at northern boundary of region I_b for various values of the pertinent parameters.

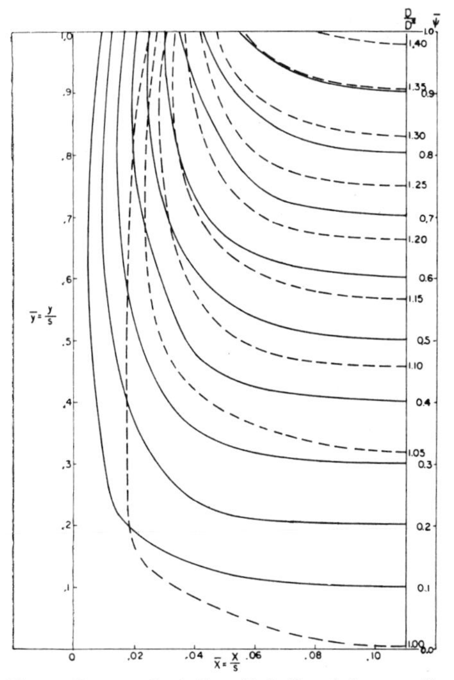

Fig. 4. Constant depth lines (dashed) and "transport" lines (solid) in region I_b for case 2a of Figs. 2 and 3 corresponding approximately of the formation of the Gulf Stream.

shows that in terms of the variables of equation (8.16) the boundary solutions $\bar{\psi}$ for a homogeneous ocean and a two-layer model are identical provided ε is large and has the same value in the two cases.

Equation (8.16) has been solved numerically for various values of ε and δ and pertinent results are plotted in Figures 2 to 4.

Figure 2 shows the variation of the dimensionless transport function $\bar{\psi}$ with dimensionless distance $\bar{X}$ from the coast at the northern boundary of region I_b. The magnitudes of β_K, U^*, s, g', D^*, ε (see legends of Figs. 2, 3) for Curve 2 a correspond to a baroclinic model of the Gulf Stream except for the fact that the southern boundary of the region I is at the equator ($\delta = 0$). The width of the Stream is, say, 150 km, a very reasonable value. Curve 2 c represents the same situation with $\delta = 1$, i.e. with the southern boundary at approximately 15° latitude. This northward shift of the southern boundary tends to produce a somewhat narrower stream, but the effect is quite small. Curve 1 b corresponds to a homogeneous ocean with the values of U^*, D^*, s and δ equal to those of the upper layer of the two-layer model of Curve 2 a. These curves thus afford a revealing comparison of the behavior of the two models. The widths of the Streams are practically the same. Thus, the question of whether the bottom surface is solid, or an interface between two layers of slightly different density in a baroclinic model, does not have much bearing on the formation of the Stream and its width. Another interesting comparison may be made between Curves 2 a and 1 a, the latter (see Section 7) corresponding to a homogeneous ocean whose depth is that of the total two-layer model with the same values of U^*, s, and δ and which therefore represents the Stream that would exist if the motion were barotropic.

Curve 2 b represents the same situation as 2 a except that the density difference is double. Comparison of the two curves demonstrates the relative insensitivity of the stream formation to this factor.

Curve 3 applies to an ocean with the same values of ε and δ as 2 a but different U^*, s, g', D^*. The drastic decrease in the width of the current may be seen from equation (8.15) to be due primarily to the increase in s.

In Figure 3 the dimensionless transport $\partial\bar{\psi}/\partial\bar{X}$ is plotted against $\bar{X}$ for the systems discussed above. The transport shows a general tendency to decrease monotonically with $\bar{X}$ due to the decrease in velocity. This tendency, however, is counterbalanced by the monotonic increase of the depth, so that in some cases the transport first increases to a maximum and then decreases. This is the case in 2 a, 2 c and 3 where the transport starts from zero due to the fact that the depth vanishes at $\bar{y} = s$, $\bar{X} = 0$ in these cases; (see the following discussion of this point). The narrow streams of cases 1 a and 3 give rise to very large transports extending over a very narrow region. The transport adjacent to the coast in the homogeneous model 1 b is much greater than that in the corresponding baroclinic model 2 a due to the latter's very small depth near the coast. The transport in 1 b drops off much more rapidly with $\bar{X}$, however, so that the widths of the streams are about equal (Fig. 2).

Figure 4 represents a typical pattern of transport and constant depth lines (case 2 a). The transport lines near the coast tend to bend away from the latter after first approaching it due to the decrease in depth near the coast. This decrease tends to cut down the transport near the coast and hence to force the stream seawards.

Our results indicate that the density stratification influences certain aspects of the stream formation, but that it is a modifying factor rather than a fundamental one insofar as our problem is concerned. One important point must be discussed in this connection, however.

Equation (8.17) shows that, for fixed y, the depth is smallest at the boundary and that it becomes zero when

$$\bar{y} = \varepsilon^{1/2} \text{ or } y^2 = \frac{D^{*2} g'}{U^* \beta_{KS}} \qquad (8.20)$$

Thus, if $\varepsilon < 1$, the solution cannot be valid for $\bar{y} > \varepsilon^{1/2}$ and the value $\bar{y} = \varepsilon^{1/2}$ might be interpreted as the latitude north of which a new regime of flow must take over. Since the velocity remains non-zero at that point we must actually except that the solution will break down at some distance south of $\bar{y} = \varepsilon^{1/2}$.

The preceding remarks apply to the behavior of the boundary solution when an arbitrarily fixed transport U^* with arbitrary depth D^* at $y = 0$ flows into the boundary region. If, however, we require that the boundary solution be matched to an interior solution the validity of which is to extend up to the eastern shore, then D^* and U^* are not independent. From equation (8.2)

$$C(L) = D^{*2} \approx D_a^2 + \frac{2\, Wa \sin K}{\varrho g'} \qquad (8.21)$$

whence, using the definitions of ε and U^x,

$$\varepsilon = \frac{D^{*2}}{D^{*2} - D_a^2} \qquad (8.22)$$

Hence, in this case $\varepsilon \geqslant 1$ and takes on its smallest value, one, only in the extreme case when $D_a = 0$. Since the meridional transport is independent of x in the interior, this extreme case would imply infinite meridional velocity at $x = a$.

It is worth noting that when the model under investigation does not represent an enclosed ocean, but rather a system in which northward flow is allowed to enter the stream across the boundary $y = 0$ so that the value of ψ on the western shore is negative, then, from equation (8.17), the depth will become zero for a value of $\bar{y}$ which is smaller than $\varepsilon^{1/2}$, so that the solution may break down for $\bar{y} < 1$ even if it is matched to an interior solution which is valid right up to $x = a$. It appears that this breakdown of the solution when ε is sufficiently small constitutes the major difference in the dynamics of the streams in a two-layer and a homogeneous model.

The theory predicts that the meridional velocity is a maximum at the western shore. This appears to violate completely the condition that a viscous fluid should adhere to a solid boundary, a condition which was specifically excluded by our approximate analysis. This violation becomes less serious than appears at first sight when one considers that the boundary may be interpreted as a water boundary with the region between the stream and the coast acting as sub-layer similar to the laminar sub-layer encountered in turbulent boundary layer flows.

Acknowledgment

The author wishes to express his gratitude to Mr. Henry Stommel of the Woods Hole Oceanographic Institution for the comments and advice offered in the course of valuable discussions without which this investigation would not have been possible.

REFERENCES

Charney, J. G., 1955: The Gulf Stream as an inertial boundary layer. *Proc. N.A.S.* (USA). **41**, No. 10, pp. 731–740.

Montgomery, R. B., 1940: The present evidence on the importance of lateral mixing processes in the Ocean. *Bull. Amer. Met. Soc.* **21**, p. 87.

Munk, W. H., 1950: On the wind-driven ocean circulation. *J. Met.* **7**, p. 79.

Munk, W. H., and Carrier, G. F., 1950: The wind-driven circulation in ocean basins of various shapes. *Tellus*, **2**, No. 3, pp. 158–167.

Stommel, H., 1955: Discussion published as a supplement to the *Journal of Marine Research*, **14**, No. 4. Also, "Why do our ideas about the ocean circulation have such a peculiarly dream-like quality?", April 1954.

Sverdrup, A. U., 1947: Wind-driven currents in a baroclinic ocean with application to the equatorial currents of the Eastern Pacific. *Proc. N.A.S.* (USA) **33**, p. 318.

On the theory of the wind-driven ocean circulation

G. F. Carrier and A. R. Robinson

Reprinted with permission from Journal of Fluid Mechanics Volume 12, Part 1, pages 49 through 80, 1962

On the theory of the wind-driven ocean circulation

By G. F. CARRIER AND A. R. ROBINSON
Pierce Hall, Harvard University

(Received 14 June 1961)

A surface distribution of stress is imposed on an ocean enclosed by two continental boundaries; the resulting transport circulation is studied between two latitudes of zero surface wind-stress curl, within which the curl reaches a single maximum. Under the assumption that turbulent transfer of relative vorticity has a minimum effect on the mean circulation, inviscid flow patterns are deduced in the limit of small transport Rossby number. Inertial currents, or naturally scaled regions of high relative vorticity, occur on both the eastern and the western continental coasts. Limits on the relative transports of the currents are obtained and found to depend on the direction of variation of the wind-stress curl with latitude, relative to that of the Coriolis accelerations. The most striking feature of the inviscid flow is a narrow inertial current the axis of which lies along the latitude of maximum wind-stress curl. All eastward flow occurs in this mid-latitude jet.

A feature of the flow which cannot remain essentially free of turbulent processes is the integrated vorticity relationship, since the imposed wind-stress distribution acts as a net source of vorticity for the ocean. Heuristic arguments are used together with this integral constraint to deduce the presence and strength of the turbulent diffusion which must occur in the region of the mid-latitude jet. It is further inferred that the turbulent meanders of the jet must effect a net meridional transport of relative vorticity.

---

1. Introduction

Considerable progress has been made in the last fourteen years towards an understanding of long-time average, large-scale ocean currents. If the sufficiently complex problem of the general ocean circulation be separated from the more fundamental problem of the circulation of the coupled atmosphere and ocean, the requirement of continuity of (turbulent) stress at the interface of the two fluids becomes the primary driving force acting upon the sea. That is, motions induced by surface wind-stress dominate those caused by the pressure gradient normal to the gravitational field caused, in turn, by the differential heating due to solar radiation. These two driving mechanisms do, of course, interact in an inherently non-linear fashion, and any separation is, to some extent, arbitrary. However, if all motion vanishes at some depth at which the internal tangential stress is also negligible, the total local horizontal transport can be related unambiguously to the surface wind-stress curl over the major part of the oceans (Sverdrup 1947). Although the assumptions inherent in the above statement are not strictly valid (Stommel 1958, chapter 11), the extremely simplified problem which they pose for the transport fields contains features which must be inherent in any more realistic model. Since those aspects of the general circulations to be discussed in this paper can be presented most simply under the assumptions of vanishing motion and stress at some constant depth, this model will be adopted here and refinements directed towards a more realistic ocean model will be left for future discussion.

Furthermore, since the quasi-geostrophic north-south transport directly forced by the wind-stress curl vanishes at certain latitudes, it has become customary to consider separately the circulation of a region bounded by two such latitudes and by two continents, e.g. the Pacific between 13° and 50° N. This point will be discussed explicitly below. In such a region, the wind-stress curl is of one sign and reaches a maximum at approximately the middle latitude, e.g. the curl reaches a maximum at about 33° N. The simplest realistic model of surface wind stress acting in such a region may be taken to have a component only in the longitudinal direction, and the longitudinal component may be taken as a function of latitude alone. This model is developed below.

The paper is presented in six sections, with some small amount of repetitive discussion, so that the more geophysically oriented sections, 2 and 3, and the more mathematically oriented sections, 4 and 5, may each be reasonably self-contained. It is clear, however, that the theory proferred depends critically on the arguments presented in all sections. For convenience the boundary-layer notation used differs somewhat in the two parts.

2. The transport theory of the general circulation

2.1. *Formulation*

To treat the simplest ocean model of this type, we consider, on the β-plane,† an ocean bounded by two latitudes at which the curl of the wind stress vanishes and by two rigid boundaries at constant longitude (meridional continents). Integrating the horizontal momentum equations and the equation of continuity between a constant level of no motion and an undistorted upper sea surface, we have

$$-\int_{-H}^{0} F_1(x,y,z)\,dz + \int_{-H}^{0} (uu_x + vu_y + wu_z)\,dz - 2\Omega f(y)\,V + \frac{1}{\rho}P_x = \tau(y), \quad (2.1)$$

$$-\int_{-H}^{0} F_2(x,y,z)\,dz + \int_{-H}^{0} (uv_x + vv_y + wv_z)\,dz + 2\Omega f(y)\,U + \frac{1}{\rho}P_y = 0, \quad (2.2)$$

$$U_x + V_y = 0, \quad (2.3)$$

where subscripts indicate partial differentiation.

† A system of rotating Cartesian co-ordinates. The rotation vector is vertical and has a variable magnitude in the latitudinal direction, thus modelling the radial component of the earth's rotation. The horizontal component is neglected, as the resulting Coriolis accelerations are relatively unimportant. To derive from spherical co-ordinates the β-plane approximation we employ, it must be assumed that the tangent of the latitude is a small quantity; thus the mean latitude of our ocean must be less than 45°. Ultimately, however, we regard the β-plane as a model system.

The following nomenclature is employed:

(x, y, z): co-ordinates in the longitudinal, latitudinal and vertical directions
(u, v, w): the corresponding velocity components
p: the pressure
ρ: the density
H: the depth below the sea surface, $z = 0$, at which motion and tangential stress are assumed to vanish
Ω: magnitude of the earth's rotation
$f(y)$: non-dimensional Coriolis parameter, i.e. $f(y) = f_0 + \beta y/b$, where $f_0 = \sin\theta_0$, $\beta = b\cos\theta_0/R$, and θ_0 is the mean latitude, b the latitudinal extent of the ocean basin, R the radius of the earth
$F_1(x, y, z)$, $F_2(x, y, z)$: components of horizontal frictional force per unit mass (lateral turbulent stresses)
$\tau(y)$: the longitudinal component of surface wind stress
$U \equiv \int_{-H}^{0} u\,dz$, $V \equiv \int_{-H}^{0} v\,dz$, $P \equiv \int_{-H}^{0} p\,dz$: the horizontal transport components and integrated pressure function

In the equations considered, ρ has been treated as a constant, an assumption compatible with the Boussinesq approximation. This, of course, is not the same as the assumption of barotropy. Note that, if the first two terms appearing on the left-hand sides of each of equations (2.1), (2.2) can be adequately represented in terms of the transport fields and their derivatives, a closed problem for the horizontal transports is formed by these three equations alone. Under such representation, these equations will form the basis of the present study, as they have for the previous studies which will first be discussed below.

A useful relationship, the vorticity equation, is obtained upon elimination of the pressure between (2.1) and (2.2),

$$\int_{-H}^{0} (F_{1y} - F_{2x})\,dz + \int_{-H}^{0} [-(uu_x + vu_y + wu_z)_y + (uv_x + vv_y + wv_z)_x]\,dz + 2\Omega\beta\,V/b = -\tau'(y). \quad (2.4)$$

No term proportional to $f(y)$ appears in the vorticity equation (2.4) because of the divergence relation (2.3). This results in the particularly significant dynamical role of the variation of effective Coriolis acceleration with latitude. For, where friction is negligible and the motion is slow enough for the neglect of non-linear terms, equation (2.4) becomes a balance between two terms only, viz.

$$2\Omega\beta V/b = -\tau'(y).$$

This is equivalent to assuming that, except for the component of internal stress necessary to transmit the surface driving force to the body of the fluid, the motion is geostrophic.

2.2. *Quasi-geostrophy*

That oceanic flow is essentially geostrophic is empirically well-known, and the frictionless, linear vorticity equation, together with mass continuity, represents the original quasi-geostrophic† model for the theoretical consideration of the transport fields developed by Sverdrup (1947). The divergence equation (2.3) may be used to define a transport stream function Ψ, in terms of which this model is represented mathematically by a single exceedingly simple equation. Let

$$U = -\Psi_y, \quad V = \Psi_x. \tag{2.5}$$

Then

$$\Psi_x = -(b/2\Omega\beta)\,\tau'(y), \tag{2.6}$$

which has the solution

$$\Psi = -(b/2\Omega\beta)\,\tau'(y)\,x + k(y), \tag{2.7}$$

where $k(y)$ is an arbitrary function of integration. Note that the latitudinal transport is completely specified by equation (2.6), and is unidirectional if $\tau'(y)$ is of one sign. On the other hand, the longitudinal transport is completely unspecified without a consideration of boundary conditions, i.e. without the determination of $k(y)$. Recall that this occurs despite the fact that the surface wind stress is purely longitudinal. It is the cross-wind component of transport which is determined and only the cross-wind component.

Since the directly forced latitudinal flow vanishes at latitudes of zero gradient of surface stress in virtue of equation (2.6), the region between two such latitudes may be considered separately from the rest of the world-ocean. This is assuming, of course, that no other mechanism induces a non-zero transport distribution along the bounding latitude circles. We shall proceed under this assumption as has been done by previous authors. Note, however, that care must be exercised when the results of such a model are applied to a discussion of the circulation of the real oceans. We return briefly to this point in §2.5 below. For simplicity we consider a rectangular ocean $0 \leqslant x \leqslant a$, $0 \leqslant y \leqslant b$, subject to the wind-stress

$$\tau(y) = -\frac{\tau_0}{\pi}\cos\frac{\pi y}{b}. \tag{2.8}$$

Thus $\tau'(y) = (\tau_0/b)\sin(\pi y/b)$ (see figure 1). The value of the stream function on the bounding latitudes may be taken as zero. To complete the description of the circulation between them, it remains only to specify that the zero stream line also lies along the eastern and western continental boundaries. However, due to the appearance of only one integration function in the solution (equation (2.7)), this is impossible. The stream function may be made zero at only one longitude. The quasi-geostrophic model is thus degenerate, in the sense that it is incapable of describing the closed circulation of an isolated ocean. This degeneracy may be recognized alternatively by noting the net transport of mass obtained upon integrating V between $x = 0$ and $x = a$ along any constant $y \neq 0$ or b. Sverdrup (1947), considering the detailed structure of equatorial currents in the eastern Pacific (in terms of a more realistic wind-stress representation), determined $k(y)$ by satisfying the boundary condition along the east-coast at $x = a$. This corresponds to a choice of $k(y) = (ab/2\Omega\beta)\,\tau'(y)$, whence

$$\Psi(x,y) = (b/2\Omega\beta)\,\tau'(y)\,(a-x). \tag{2.9}$$

† The term quasi-geostrophic is used throughout this paper precisely as defined here, n.b. *not* as commonly used in meteorology.

Empirical motivation for this choice lies in the fact that at low latitudes strong currents form and flow along the western boundaries, e.g. the Kuroshio. It may be anticipated, therefore, that, at low latitudes, the region near the western coast is dynamically more complicated than that near the eastern coast.

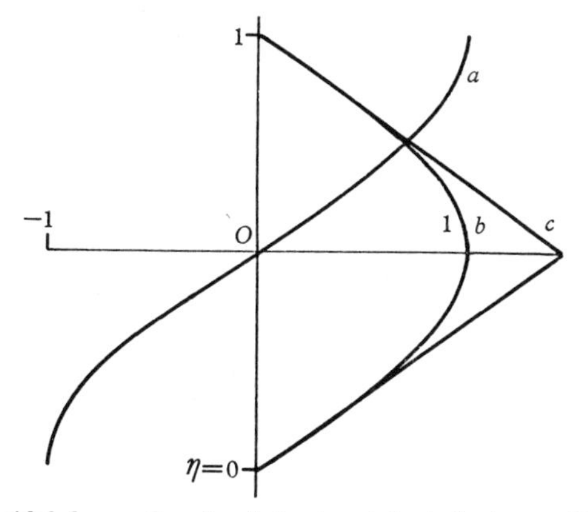

FIGURE 1. (*a*) Sinusoidal form of a simple horizontal wind stress; (*b*) the corresponding latitudinal gradient (wind-stress curl); (*c*) the triangular approximation to the curl as employed in § 3.

The quasi-geostrophic degeneracy must be removed by including at least some of the terms neglected in the vorticity equation (2.4), which, in its complete form, is certainly capable of describing a closed ocean circulation. The terms to be included will still remain small over most of the area of the ocean, but will become controlling in certain limited regions, e.g. boundary layers near coasts. Thus the simple balance given by equation (2.6) will still obtain almost everywhere. It is important to note, however, that since $k(y)$ is determined only by a consideration of the singular regions, the processes of friction and/or inertia (which are directly important only in limited regions) have a gross effect on the flow everywhere. Only after the details of the singular regions have been considered is the east-west transport, $U = b(2\Omega\beta)^{-1}\tau''(y)\,x - k'(y)$, known in the quasi-geostrophic region. It is found that $k(y)$ depends strongly on the assumptions made to relate the integrated frictional and inertial terms to the mean transport fields.

2.3. *The diffusion of relative vorticity*

The first models which yielded complete solutions for closed oceanic vortices were made under the assumption that the inertial terms (the non-linear coupling of the mean field with itself) remained negligible. The system was closed by the inclusion of horizontal turbulent friction (the non-linear coupling of the zero-average fluctuation fields). This was originally done most simply under the assumption of a frictional force proportional to the horizontal transport velocity (Stommel 1948), and later developed under the assumption of a constant horizontal eddy coefficient (Munk 1950). The mathematical statements are, respectively,

$$\int_{-H}^{0} F_1\,dz = RU, \quad \int_{-H}^{0} F_2\,dz = RV \quad \text{and} \quad \int_{-H}^{0} F_1\,dz = \nu\nabla^2 U, \quad \int_{-H}^{0} F_2\,dz = \nu\nabla^2 V,$$

where R and ν are free parameters, adjusted, in each case, to give the best fit to observations. The equations governing the two models are

$$R\nabla^2\Psi + 2\Omega\beta\Psi_x/b = -\tau'(y)$$

and

$$\nu\nabla^4\Psi + 2\Omega\beta\Psi_x/b = -\tau'(y).$$

Both equations are linear and tractable. For the trigonometric wind distribution given by (2.8), Ψ may be taken proportional to sin $(\pi y/b)$ and the equations separated.† If R and ν be assumed small, the resulting x-equations are simply soluble by the technique of singular perturbation theory (Munk & Carrier 1950). To apply this technique, the ocean is initially separated into three regions, an interior and a boundary-layer region near each coast, i.e. at $x = 0, a$. The appropriate interior approximation is that of quasi-geostrophy, and the interior solution is given again by (2.7). In the boundary-layer regions the flow is approximately free from the direct (local) wind stress, a balance being obtained in the vorticity equation primarily between frictional and variation-of-Coriolis-parameter terms. Formally joining the boundary-layer solutions to the interior, the solution is completed and $k(y)$ is unambiguously determined. It is deduced for both models that, in a formal first approximation, the contribution from the boundary layer along the eastern coast vanishes identically. Thus $k(y)$ is determined from the interior solution satisfying by itself the condition $\Psi = 0$ at $x = a$, and the quasi-geostrophic interior is again given by (2.9). The streamline pattern for the asymmetric vortex is sketched in figure 2*b*. Mathematically the difference between the eastern and western coastal regions results from the fact that the boundary-layer equations consist of a balance between an even and an odd x-derivative. This results in a single sign change between the eastern and western regions when the equations are expressed in terms of local longitudinal variables positive in the direction of outward normals from the coasts (the boundary-layer variables).

In terms of the frictional models, a complete theoretical description of a general ocean circulation was for the first time achieved. Although not at all satisfactorily treating the turbulent process involved, the constant-eddy-viscosity model was considered the more plausible one, and was developed in some detail, including a realistic treatment of wind-stress distributions and ocean-basin shapes. As in the simple model discussed above, the interior solution satisfies alone the eastern boundary condition. An important consequence is that at each latitude the transport of the western boundary current is completely specified independently of the eddy viscosity, and is given by $\psi(0,y)$ of equation (2.9). The width of the western boundary current does, however, depend on the eddy viscosity, and is appropriately measured by the length $(\nu a/2\Omega)^{\frac{1}{3}}$. The eddy viscosity is then determined by making this length scale agree with observation.

The frictional ocean model described above does yield a westward oriented asymmetrical vortex as the response to a simple wind stress, but as an acceptable

† The higher order of the differential equation for the model with constant eddy viscosity implies that additional boundary conditions have to be specified. These are taken as $\partial\Psi/\partial x = 0$, $x = 0, a$; $\partial^2\Psi/\partial y^2 = 0$, $y = 0, b$; i.e. rigid, and tangential-stress-free surfaces respectively. The separation of Ψ is seen to remain valid.

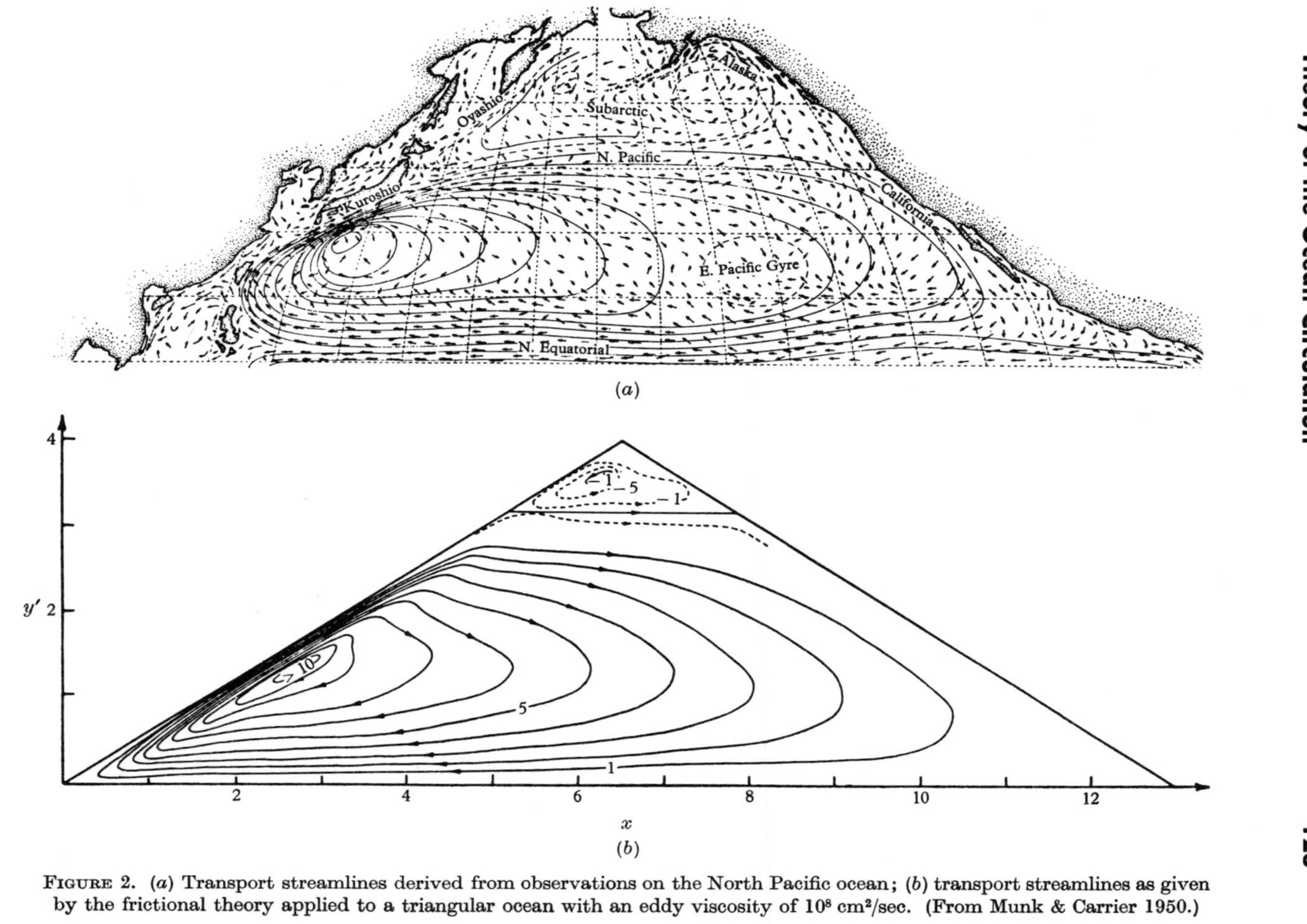

FIGURE 2. (a) Transport streamlines derived from observations on the North Pacific ocean; (b) transport streamlines as given by the frictional theory applied to a triangular ocean with an eddy viscosity of 10^8 cm^2/sec. (From Munk & Carrier 1950.)

theory of the general circulation in the real oceans it is open to several criticisms. First, the eddy viscosity required to give the observed width of the Gulf Stream to the theoretical boundary current is significantly greater than the value of the eddy viscosity indicated in the Gulf Stream region by independent means. Secondly, the theoretically deduced transports of the western boundary currents are much smaller than observed transports, smaller by a factor of 0·5 for the Gulf Stream and 0·6 for the Kuroshio (Munk 1950, table 2). Thirdly, the predicted streamline pattern is in qualitative disagreement with observations. This may be seen from figure 2, which compares the theory applied to the North Pacific Ocean with the observed transport field. Since the only strong current predicted on the frictional theory flows northward along the entire length of the western boundary, the observed Kuroshio may be accounted for below about 35°. The theory cannot, however, explain the Kuroshio leaving the coast at this latitude and, holding together, flowing eastward out to sea; nor does it account for the California or the Alaska currents. It has been speculated that the Kuroshio leaves the western coast because of an instability of the simple flow given by the frictional theory. The circulation which includes the Alaska current has been considered to be an independent vortex, which appears in the apex of the triangular ocean of figure 2*b*. It may be seen that the theoretical gyre begins at too high a latitude, is too small, and has only a western boundary current.

2.4. *The advection of relative vorticity*

The above discrepancies preclude the possibility of a purely frictional theory of the general ocean circulation. This possibility is precluded even if one is seeking only an approximate explanation of the grossest features of the motions which occur in nature. This means that the boundary-layer control of the general ocean circulation cannot be dominated by the frictional diffusion of vorticity. It must, therefore, be dominated by the non-linear process of vorticity advection. Initial work on the development of such an inertial theory (Charney 1955; Morgan 1956) seems to have been motivated only by the discrepancy between the theoretically required eddy-viscosity and the observational upper bound,† under the stimulation of the results of a very simple inertial model (the conservation of potential vorticity in a current independent of latitude, see Stommel 1958, p. 109) which provided a suggestively accurate description of a western boundary current. An immediate advantage of a thoery in which the inertial terms completely dominate the frictional ones is that no free parameter, characterizing the turbulence, is present. It is possible to subject the theory to stringent comparison with nature.

Due to the non-linearity of the inertial terms, it is not possible to develop in a straightforward manner a theory for the transport fields alone. We shall

† If one accepts 10^6 cm²/sec obtained from Pillsbury's measurements in the Florida Straits (Stommel 1955) as characteristic of the maximum turbulence present in the boundary-current region, then the 10^8 cm²/sec required by the frictional theory is larger than that which is available. If, on the other hand, one is willing to accept a narrower stream from the theory and uses 10^6 cm²/sec, the inertial terms are of comparable magnitude to the viscous terms. The frictional theory as developed is thus not self-consistent, and it becomes reasonable to explore next the restriction $\nu \ll 10^6$.

proceed to do so, however, by evaluating the integrated inertial terms by means of an assumption; thus we replace equation (2.4) by

$$H^{-1}[-(UU_x+VU_y)_y+(UV_x+VV_y)_x]+2\Omega\beta V/b+\tau'(y) = 0. \qquad (2.10)$$

In other words, we replace the actual problem of interest, that of a three-dimensional flow driven by a surface force, by an analogous problem of a two-dimensional flow driven by a body force. The approximate evaluation of the advective integrals inherent in the analogy is, of course, valid only when the vertical velocity and the vertical variation of the horizontal velocity are negligible. These conditions certainly are not fulfilled over the major part of the ocean in the presence of the wind-driven surface Ekman layer and the corresponding convergence or divergence. But over the major part of the ocean, the inertial terms will be anyhow negligible, becoming important only in intense and narrow currents. These streams of high relative vorticity are not driven primarily by the local winds (divergence of the local Ekman layer), but by a horizontal flux of mass into the region of the intense current. This horizontal mass flux has originated from the effect of the winds blowing over the whole ocean basin. Furthermore, the downstream component of flow in the narrow current remains approximately geostrophic. Under these conditions, equation (2.10) provides an appropriate approximation everywhere for the upper layer of a two-layer theory. Although it is necessary in a proper two-layer theory to allow for a variation in depth of the upper layer, i.e. to let $H = H(x, y)$, we shall treat only the case of constant H. In terms of the understanding of the relationship between the quasi-geostrophic regions and the streams of high relative vorticity provided by this simple example, a more sophisticated model may be evolved.

In the previous theories mentioned above, the depth of the upper layer was treated as variable. The studies were not, however, concerned with a complete inertial theory in the sense of the determination of $k(y)$ and the associated quasi-geostrophic flow by a simultaneous consideration of boundary-layer and interior regions. They were concerned rather with the investigation of particular features of inertial boundary currents with a given interior flow. Furthermore, consideration was given only to the flow in the equatorial half of an ocean basin, the region below the maximum of the wind-stress curl. It will be seen below that results so obtained are not in general valid over the entire basin.

Both studies were influenced by the fact that in previous ocean models the interior stream function satisfied by itself the eastern coast boundary condition. Charney assumes that the interior solution should in fact be given by the Sverdrup–Munk transport function, but noting that the transport prescribed into the Gulf Stream region is too low on this theory, replaces it by the observed transport function at the Gulf Stream edge. With this empirical interior Charney computed by numerical integration the structure of a boundary current in a two-layer inertial model which allowed for variation in depth of the upper layer. He found good agreement with the observed structure of the Gulf Stream. The good agreement obtained by a proper local theory provides some justification for our cruder treatment of the inertial terms when we consider the complete problem.

Morgan considered a greater range of particular types of inertial boundary layers. None were as directly applicable to a real oceanic situation as was Charney's study, but were coupled with theoretically deduced interior solutions. To simplify the non-linear analysis, the wind-stress curl was approximated by a linear function away from the lowest latitude. For a constant layer-depth Morgan considered two choices of interior solution, the Sverdrup–Munk solution satisfying the eastern coast boundary condition, $k(y) = (ab/2\Omega\beta)\tau'(y)$, and a solution which satisfied the western coast boundary condition, $k(y) = 0$. For the first case the flow could be closed by an inertial boundary current, for the second it could not. Then, retaining the satisfaction of the eastern condition by the interior function, the effects of density stratification in terms of a variable layer-depth were investigated. The existence and width of the boundary current were not markedly altered by the variable depth. The transport of the western boundary current is, of course, independent of whether or not H is varied when the interior function is assumed to satisfy the east coast conditions. Under this assumption, the interior function is the same as that deduced on the frictional theory, and the transport discrepancy is assumed in Morgan's model.

Before proceeding to develop an inertial theory in which the interior and boundary-layer solutions are treated in full generality, we shall first explore more fully the case of linear wind-stress curl as posed by Morgan. The analysis will remain quite straightforward and the results will exemplify the features of greatest interest of the complete inertial theory. A more general interior solution (which contains Morgan's two solutions as special cases) will be used. Morgan's solution for an equatorial half-basin will be shown to be the end-point of a class of possible solutions and it will be shown that Morgan's choice corresponds to that of minimum transport in the western boundary current. Considering similarly the poleward half of an ocean basin, significantly different constraints on the class of interior solutions allowed will be obtained. Combining these results to infer the flow over a complete ocean basin, the most striking feature is the existence of a strong and narrow eastward flowing current at the latitude of maximum wind-stress curl.

The determination of $k(y)$ is, although in a highly non-linear fashion, related to the solutions of equation (2.10) when the forcing inhomogeneity, $\tau'(y)$, vanishes identically. Such free inertial flow has been considered by Fofonoff (1954). Although we shall not make direct use of the free solutions in our following development, in the free solutions geostrophic regions of high relative vorticity are related to one another in a general way which is characteristic of the forced problem. A discussion of the free problem is presented in the next section.

2.5. *Free inertial flow*

We consider here solutions of equation (2.9) for the case of $\tau'(y) \equiv 0$. Introducing the stream function as defined by (2.5), the terms may be arranged in the form

$$\Psi_x\{\nabla^2\Psi + 2\Omega h f(y)\}_y - \Psi_y\{\nabla^2\Psi + 2\Omega h f(y)\}_x = 0. \qquad (2.11)$$

Simple integration gives the first integral in the form

$$\nabla^2\Psi + 2\Omega h f = G(\Psi). \qquad (2.12)$$

As was done by Fofonoff, we shall investigate only the class of free solutions for which (2.12) becomes linear, i.e. we investigate the case of

$$G(\Psi) = g_0 + g_1 \Psi, \tag{2.13}$$

where g_0 and g_1 are numerical constants (a velocity and an inverse squared length respectively, recalling that Ψ is a transport stream function). We seek conditions under which the free solution will contain a geostrophic region and regions of high relative vorticity, i.e. inertial currents, retaining the conditions that Ψ vanish on all sides of a bounding rectangle.

Let the stream-function be non-dimensionalized by its maximum value Ψ_0, which is of course indeterminate for a free solution. We introduce also non-dimensional longitude and latitude variables; by substitution of (2.13), (2.12) becomes

$$\alpha\gamma_1(\lambda^2\phi_{\xi\xi} + \phi_{\eta\eta}) - \gamma_1\phi - \gamma_0 + \eta = 0, \tag{2.14}$$

where $\Psi = \Psi_0\phi, \quad x = a\xi, \quad y = b\eta,$

and $\gamma_0 = (f_0 - g_0 h^{-1})/\beta, \quad \gamma_1 = g_1\Psi_0/2\Omega\beta h, \quad \alpha = g_1/b^2, \quad \lambda = a/b.$

The conditions under which a geostrophic region and singular regions of narrow inertial currents can exist may now be extracted. For succinctness we shall exclude extreme geometry, i.e. we assume the length to width ratio of the ocean basin, λ, to be of order unity. Then a geostrophic region will exist if $|\alpha| \ll 1$, the approximate solution to (2.14) being given by

$$\phi_g = (\eta - \gamma_0)/\gamma_1. \tag{2.15}$$

Note that the geostrophic stream function is zero only on $\eta = \gamma_0$, so that at least three inertial boundary layers are required to yield a complete free solution. The non-dimensional width of the inertial boundary layers will be $O(\alpha^{\frac{1}{2}})$, irrespective of whether the layers are near bounding latitudes or longitude. The condition that the resulting approximate equation describe a boundary-layer phenomenon, i.e. a narrow current, is that its solution contains a decaying real exponential. This condition is seen to be $\alpha > 0$. A solution with a natural length scale $O(|\alpha|^{\frac{1}{2}})$ but for which $\alpha < 0$ is indeed possible; it would have the form of a rapidly oscillating inertial wave existing over the entire ocean basin. Such solutions are certainly of interest but will not be discussed further here.

In summary, note that both conditions obtained are in the nature of restrictions upon α, and may be expressed as

$$0 < \alpha = g_1 b^{-2} \ll 1. \tag{2.16}$$

Thus the existence of a geostrophic region which can be closed by inertial boundary layers, and the characterization of these boundary layers, depends only upon the integration function $G(\Psi)$. In particular, there is no fundamental dependence upon β, the variation of the Coriolis parameter with latitude. This fact is not clearly stated by Fofonoff. What does depend on β, however, is the nature of the geostrophic interior.

From (2.15) the geostrophic velocities are expressed as

$$U_g = -2\Omega\beta h/g_1, \quad V_g = 0. \tag{2.17}$$

Thus, if $\beta = 0$, the motion is confined entirely to the boundary layers. If $\beta \neq 0$, from (2.17) and (2.16), the geostrophic region consists of a uniform westward flow. Thus, as found by Fofonoff, all eastward flow must occur in a narrow current of high relative vorticity. We restate these results in more general terms which will be useful for a comparison with the problem of the forced flow as follows: Considering only the geostrophic region, the north–south flow is completely determined ($V = 0$), but not the east–west flow ($U \sim g_1^{-1}$). If we insist that inertial boundary layers exist which will close the geostrophic flow, the (direction of the) east–west flow is determined ($g_1 > 0$). The geostrophic flow can only be westward.

A simple flow pattern obtained by Fofonoff is shown in figure 3. Note the symmetrical appearance of northward and southward flowing western and eastern coast boundary currents, as well as the necessary asymmetry of the eastward flowing boundary current. This eastward jet has been placed on the northern boundary, i.e. the choice of $\gamma_0 = 0$ has been made. This is, of course, completely arbitrary; there is no uniqueness associated with a free solution. The eastward flow could occur on the southern boundary or in a free inertial jet at any intermediary latitude.

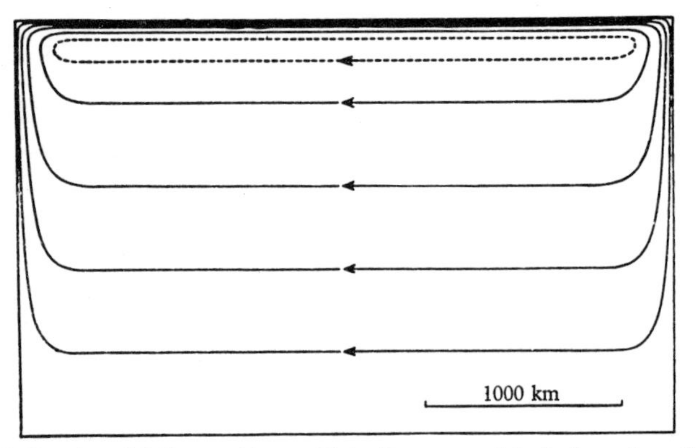

FIGURE 3. A free inertial flow pattern. Note the symmetrical character of the north–south flow in the boundary layers along the eastern and western coasts. (From Fofonoff 1954.)

A useful application of the free solutions discussed here lies in the case of fluid motion which is driven by a distribution of sources and sinks imposed along its boundaries. Some special cases have been studied; in particular if a point source is placed at $\xi = 1$, $\eta = 1$ and a point sink of equal strength at $\xi = 1$, $\eta = 0$, the resulting circulation may have a boundary current along the eastern coast which is stronger than the boundary current along the western coast. The relevance of these remarks to the general ocean circulation lies in the fact that ocean basins do communicate with one another across latitudes of zero wind-stress curl, and such communication can be modelled by a source-sink distribution. This problem will be developed elsewhere, for systems driven simultaneously by wind-stress and source-sink distributions. The results are particularly relevant for southern-hemisphere oceans, e.g. they may account for the otherwise ambiguously large transport of the Benguela Current.

3. A completely inertial model

3.1. *Development for a simple wind system*

We proceed to discuss the type of forced flow allowed in an ocean basin driven by a wind-stress curl which has a maximum at some mid-latitude. The flow is assumed to have a quasi-geostrophic region and to be closed by inertial boundary layers; thus the stream-function will everywhere satisfy equation (2.10). Introducing non-dimensional variables and parameters, (2.10) takes the form

$$\epsilon[\psi_\xi(\psi_{\xi\xi}+\lambda^2\psi_{\eta\eta})_\eta-\psi_\eta(\psi_{\xi\xi}+\lambda^2\psi_{\eta\eta})_\xi]+\psi_\xi+g(\eta)=0, \tag{3.1}$$

where $\psi=(2\Omega\beta/\tau_0 a)\Psi, \quad g=(b/\tau_0)\tau', \quad \epsilon=\tau_0[ah(2\Omega\beta)^2]^{-1},$

and ξ, η, λ have been defined following equation (2.14). The transport Rossby number, ϵ, appears as the singular perturbation parameter. For the typical values $\tau_0 = 1\,\text{cm}^2\,\text{sec}^{-1}$, $a = 10^9\,\text{cm}$, $h = 10^5\,\text{cm}$, $2\Omega = 1{\cdot}4\times10^{-4}\,\text{sec}^{-1}$, $\beta = 0{\cdot}7$, we have $\epsilon = O(10^{-6})$.

The interior solution to (3.1) is obtained formally by assuming that ψ is a smooth function of (ξ, η) and thereby neglecting the ϵ-terms. We write this as

$$\psi_I(\xi,\eta)=g(\eta)[-\xi+l(\eta)], \tag{3.2}$$

where $g(\eta)\,l(\eta)$ is the non-dimensional form of $k(y)$ as discussed in §1. The form (3.2) shows clearly that ψ^I may be zero upon one curve, $\xi = l(\eta)$, in the longitude-latitude plane, and is also convenient because we shall continue to assume that $\psi(\xi,0)=\psi(\xi,1)=0$ because $g(0)=g(1)=0$. In general, however, since ψ_I may not be made zero at $\xi = 0, 1$, we must allow for boundary layers near both the eastern and western coasts (signified by subscripts E and W respectively). Introducing the boundary-layer variables $\zeta_E=\epsilon^{-\frac{1}{2}}\xi, \zeta_W=\epsilon^{-\frac{1}{2}}(1-\xi)$, and recognizing that the amplitudes of ψ_E and ψ_W cannot depend upon ϵ since they must join to ψ_I as given by (3.2), the boundary-layer equation is

$$\psi_\zeta\psi_{\zeta\zeta\eta}-\psi_\eta\psi_{\zeta\zeta\zeta}+\psi_\zeta=0, \tag{3.3}$$

for either E or W subscript. Equation (3.3) is correct to $O(\epsilon^{\frac{1}{2}})$, the relative vorticity is approximated by Ψ_{xx} and the characteristic longitudinal length scale is $\epsilon^{\frac{1}{2}}a$ or tens of kilometres.

Since the boundary-layer stream functions are locally free, equation (3.3) may be integrated in the manner of §2.6, equations (2.11), (2.12), to yield

$$\psi_{\zeta\zeta}+\eta=H(\psi). \tag{3.4}$$

In this case, however, the function $H(\psi)$ must be determined by joining to the interior solution at the boundary-layer edge in each case. The problem is complicated by the fact that the interior solution is itself not known because of the arbitrary function $l(\eta)$ appearing in (3.2). In the case of non-uniqueness, which we anticipate, the joining of the boundary layers to the interior provides relationships between the functions H_E, H_W and l which serve to restrict the interior and boundary layers allowed. To proceed simply at this point we consider only the class of interior stream functions that will be zero at some constant longitude, which may in general lie inside, outside or on a boundary of the ocean basin, i.e. we let

$$\psi_I = g(\eta)(-\xi+P), \tag{3.5}$$

where P is a numerical constant.

The flow patterns allowed by the coupling of inertial boundary layers with quasi-geostrophic regions will be found to be of two distinct types. These types are distinguished by whether the driving force $\tau'(y)$ varies with latitude in the same or opposite manner as the Coriolis parameter $f(y)$, i.e. depending upon the sign of $\tau''(y)/\beta$. We consider here the two simplest possibilities, by letting $\tau'(y)$ vary linearly with latitude in each case. For a single ocean basin, the two cases occur below and above the latitude of maximum wind-stress curl. Expanding $\tau'(y)$, as given by equation (2.8), about the southern and northern bounding latitudes, we obtain the relations:

near $y = 0$,

$$\tau'(y) = \frac{\tau_0}{b}\sin\frac{\pi y}{b} \doteqdot \frac{\tau_0 \pi}{b^2}y = \frac{\tau_0}{b}\pi\eta \equiv \frac{\tau_0}{b}g^+(\eta), \tag{3.6a}$$

and near $y = b$,

$$\tau'(y) \doteqdot \frac{\tau_0\pi}{b^2}(b-y) = \frac{\tau_0}{b}\pi(1-\eta) \equiv \frac{\tau_0}{b}g^-(\eta) \tag{3.6b}$$

(see figure 1c). The superscripts $\pm$ have been introduced to distinguish between the regions where the driving force has the same or the opposite sign as β. The allowed flow patterns will now be discussed in terms of the four functions $H^{\pm}_{E,W}$ and the two interior constants $P^{\pm}$.

Case I: an equatorward half-basin

At the edge of each boundary layer, the relative vorticity becomes negligible. Setting $\psi_{\zeta\zeta} = 0$ in (3.4) and using (3.2) evaluated in terms of (3.6a), we have at the western and eastern coasts

$$\eta = H^+_W[\psi^+_I(0,\eta)] = H^+_W(\pi\eta P^+), \tag{3.7a}$$

$$\eta = H^+_E[\psi^+_I(1,\eta)] = H^+_E[\pi\eta(P^+-1)], \tag{3.7b}$$

whence $$H^+_W(\psi_W) = (1/\pi P^+)\psi_W, \quad H^+_E(\psi_E) = [1/\pi(P^+-1)]\psi_E. \tag{3.8a, b}$$

If we insert the functions (3.8a, b) into their respective boundary-layer equations obtained from (3.4), we obtain the equations

$$\psi_{\zeta\zeta}-(1/\pi P^+)\psi+\eta = 0, \quad \psi_{\zeta\zeta}-[1/\pi(P^+-1)]\psi+\eta = 0, \tag{3.9a, b}$$

where the subscripts E, W have been omitted on ψ, ζ of (3.9a, b) respectively. The condition that equations (3.9a, b) be of boundary-layer form, i.e. contain a real decaying exponential rather than only oscillatory homogeneous solutions is that the term in ψ alone be of opposite sign to the second derivative term. Thus, from (3.9a), $P^+ > 0$, and from (3.9b), $P^+-1 > 0$, will ensure that inertial boundary layers exist. It is seen that the eastern-coast condition is the strongest and contains the western-coast condition.

Case II: a poleward half-basin

We now use (3.6*b*) and proceed as above. Thus

$$\eta = H_W^-[\psi_I^-(0,\eta)] = H_W^-[\pi(1-\eta)P^-], \tag{3.10a}$$

$$\eta = H_E^-[\psi_I^-(1,\eta)] = H_E^-[\pi(1-\eta)(P^- -1)], \tag{3.10b}$$

whence

$$H_W^-(\psi_W) = -(1/\pi P^-)\psi_W + 1, \quad H_E^-(\psi_E) = -[1/\pi(P^- -1)]\psi_E + 1, \tag{3.11a, b}$$

and

$$\psi_{\zeta\zeta} + (1/\pi P^-)\psi + \eta - 1 = 0, \quad \psi_{\zeta\zeta} + [1/\pi(P^- -1)]\psi + \eta - 1 = 0, \tag{3.12a, b}$$

again omitting the subscripts W, E respectively from the last two equations. For boundary-layer form, the restrictions are $P^- < 0$, $P^- - 1 < 0$. Thus in this case the western-coast condition is seen to be strongest and to contain the eastern-coast condition, in opposition to the result for case I.

Under the stated restrictions, equations (3.9*a*, *b*) and (3.12*a*, *b*) have simple exponential solutions with $\psi = 0$ at $\zeta = 0$; they join smoothly to the interior function as $\zeta \to \infty$, e.g.

$$\psi_E^+ = \pi\eta(P^+ - 1)[1 - \exp\{-[\pi(P^+ - 1)]^{-\frac{1}{2}}\zeta_E\}]. \tag{3.13}$$

Therefore the most general interior solutions of the form (3.5) are

$$\psi_I^+ = \pi\eta(-\xi + P^+) \quad (P^+ > 1); \quad \psi_I^- = \pi(1-\eta)(-\xi + P^-) \quad (P^- < 0). \tag{3.14a, b}$$

Correspondingly, the east-west component of quasi-geostrophic transport may be obtained as

$$U_I^+ = -\frac{\partial}{\partial\eta}\psi_I^+ = -\pi(-\xi + P^+) \quad (P^+ > 1), \tag{3.15a}$$

$$U_I^- = -\frac{\partial}{\partial\eta}\psi_I^- = \pi(-\xi + P^-) \quad (P^- < 0). \tag{3.15b}$$

The values of U as obtained from (3.15*a*) and (3.15*b*) are seen to be everywhere negative, as the ocean basin is contained in $0 < \xi < 1$. Thus the requirement that inertial boundary layers exist to close the quasi-geostrophic flow has served to determine the direction of the east–west flow in the quasi-geostrophic region. The flow must always be to the west (compare the discussion of §2.5, following equation (2.17)). The wind system giving rise to the $\tau'(y)$ which we have considered is westward in the equatorward half-basin and eastward in the poleward half-basin. Thus in one case the longitudinal component of oceanic transport is in the direction of the wind and in the other case it is opposite to the direction of the wind. This is due to the interaction of the directly forced flow with the inertial boundary currents. We reiterate that a longitudinal wind determines only the latitudinal oceanic transport quasi-geostrophically.

The above results have a profound implication for the qualitative structure of allowed flow patterns over an entire ocean basin, in which there can be no net flow to the west. As will be demonstrated in §4, curvature in the wind-stress curl will not allow an eastward flow. There must, therefore, be a breakdown of quasi-geostrophic dynamics at the latitude of the maximum of $\tau'(y)$ (where $\tau''(y)$ changes sign relative to β). The eastward flow must occur in a region of high relative vorticity, i.e. in a free inertial jet. Thus the fact that the Gulf Stream and Kuroshio leave the coast and flow eastward out to sea is simply explained by a complete inertial theory. An intense current at the latitude of maximum wind-stress curl is a required feature of all allowed flow patterns.

The simple results obtained here contain additional implications for the number and the transport of the inertial currents along the eastern and western coasts. In the equatorward half-basin there must be at least a western boundary current; the interior solution can satisfy the east-coast condition ($P^+ = 1$), but not the west-coast condition. In the poleward half-basin there must be at least an eastern boundary current; the interior solution can satisfy the west-coast condition ($P^- = 0$), but not the east-coast condition. In general, however, there will be both eastern and western boundary currents in both half basins. The direction of flow must be to the north and in the equatorward western current and the poleward-eastern current, and to the south in the equatorward-eastern and the poleward-western currents.

A final physical interpretation of the allowed $P^\pm$ values lies in the transports $T^\pm_{E,W}$ of the boundary currents. These may be determined entirely from the interior solution (3.14a, b) since ψ is zero on all coasts; hence we obtain

$$\left.\begin{aligned} T^+_W &= \psi^+_I(0,\eta) = \pi\eta P^+, \quad & T^+_E &= \psi^+_I(1,\eta) = \pi\eta(P^+ - 1), \\ T^-_W &= \pi(1-\eta)P^-, \quad & T^-_E &= \pi(1-\eta)(P^- - 1). \end{aligned}\right\} \tag{3.16}$$

Therefore, in the equatorward half-basin, the western current must always have greater transport than the eastern current, and in the poleward half-basin the eastern current must always have greater transport than the western current. What happens is that in each half-basin the boundary current which must always be present transports the amount of fluid directly forced by the wind, as well as sharing in a recirculation phenomenon involving also the mid-latitude current, the other boundary current, and a broad flow across the major part of the ocean. It should be noted that the transport discrepancy for the Gulf Stream and Kuroshio which one obtains using the frictional theory discussed in §2.3 is not contained in the inertial theory. The Sverdrup–Munk transport function corresponds to the case $P^+ = 1$. As this is the minimum allowed value of P^+ it yields the minimum allowed value of T^+_W, which may be arbitrarily larger.

The lack of uniqueness inherent in this discussion is a real feature of a complete steady-state inertial theory. The ambiguity will, however, be partially removed by the inclusion of additional physics when the effects of friction are considered. It will be shown that an eastern boundary current in the equatorward half-basin is required and correspondingly that the minimum allowed value for T^+_W is greater than the Sverdrup–Munk transport.

In figure 4, a sketch is presented of the simplest stream-line pattern allowed by the inertial theory, for $P^+ = 1$, $P^- = 0$. Note that (for a northern-hemisphere ocean) the mid-latitude jet is fed from the north and discharges to the south. Note, however, that there is no transport across the zero stream-line which forms the axis of the jet, i.e. on a completely inertial model, the half-basins do not communicate. The striking difference between this pattern and Sverdrup–Munk transport streamlines may be seen from figure 2*b*. Since, in general, boundary currents will be present also on the north-western and south-eastern coasts, a schematic comparison with figure 2*a* shows that the Kuroshio, the Kuroshio extension or North Pacific current, the California current, the Alaska current and the Oyashio may be simply explained on the inertial theory.

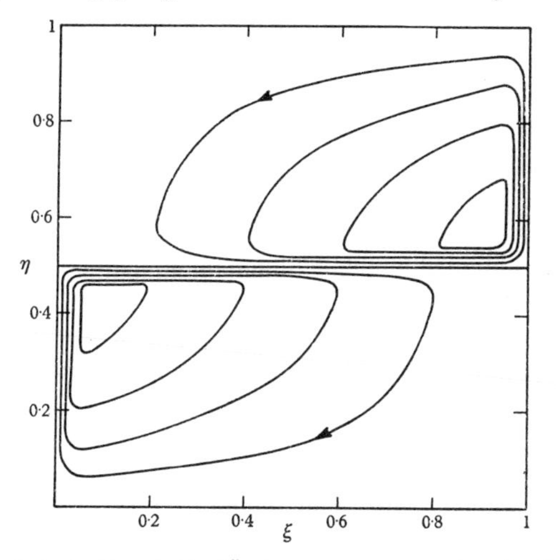

FIGURE 4. Transport streamlines in the (ξ, η) square ocean as given by the inertial theory. The double gyre with a mid-latitude inertial jet is the simplest response to the trigonometric wind-stress curl of figure 1*b*.

3.2. *The mid-latitude jet*

Since the broad flow over the open ocean transports mass only to the west, the transport to the east must occur in a region of high relative vorticity. This inertial current must occur at about the latitude of maximum wind-stress curl, and will be 'free' in the sense that no physical boundary or local boundary condition is directly forcing the singular region to occur there. In the sense that there must occur an influx and efflux of mass along the sides of the jet, it will not be free. To explore the dynamics and scale of such a jet we shall assume in this section that the direction of the strong current is purely longitudinal, i.e. that large gradients occur only in the latitudinal direction.

An unusual feature of the dynamics of this current system is that the variation of the Coriolis parameter is of primary importance, even though the phenomenon occurs within a latitude belt less than 100 km in width. This is because the importance of the β-effect is not measured directly by the percentage variation of f over the latitudinal extent of the current, but is measured rather by the contribution to the overall vorticity balance made by the planetary vorticity tendency, $\beta\Psi_x$, in the region. Over the major part of the ocean, both north and south of the narrow current, the advection of relative vorticity is completely negligible with respect to the planetary vorticity tendency. The width of the current is a natural scale whereby the advection becomes comparable. This is similar in principle to the vorticity balance in a coastal inertial current, but differs in that in a coastal current $\beta\Psi_x$ becomes larger than in the open ocean, while in the mid-latitude current it does not. Correspondingly, the relative vorticity (as a point function of latitude and longitude) is larger in a coastal jet, but since the mid-latitude jet is broader, the total vorticity transport by both types of currents will be the same order of magnitude (with respect to dependence upon the Rossby number, ϵ).

To present a formal description, we introduce a scaled latitudinal variable, and obtain the approximate form of equation (3.1), which becomes

$$\lambda^2(\psi^J_\xi \psi^J_{XXX} - \psi^J_X \psi^J_{\xi XX}) + \psi^J_\xi + g(\eta_0) = 0, \tag{3.17}$$

where $X = \epsilon^{-\frac{1}{3}}(\eta - \eta_0)$, and the superscript J refers to the region of the mid-latitude jet. The amplitude of ψ must again be independent of ϵ in order to join to the solutions on either side of the jet. The equation is correct to $O(\epsilon^{\frac{2}{3}})$. The dependence upon λ can, of course, be removed by a scaling transformation to a latitudinal variable $\lambda^{-\frac{2}{3}}X$.

It is of some interest to demonstrate that equation (3.17) may be reduced to an ordinary differential equation by means of a similarity transformation. Since such a transformation depends upon the interior function of the transverse variable at the boundary-layer edge, and since this function must differ on the poleward and equatorward sides of the jet, it is necessary to introduce separate variables to measure distance away from the central zero-streamline in each direction. We illustrate by the equatorward directed similarity transformation. Using an interior solution ψ^+_I of the form (3.5) and the notation

$$g(\eta_0) = g_0, \quad s = X[\lambda^2(\xi - P^+)]^{-\frac{1}{3}}, \quad \psi^J = (\xi - P^+)\,[F(s) - g_0], \tag{3.18}$$

(3.17) transforms to

$$g_0 F'''' - F'''F + \tfrac{1}{3}F'F'' + \tfrac{1}{3}sF' + F = 0, \tag{3.19}$$

where a prime denotes total differentiation with respect to s. The boundary conditions are $F(\infty) = 0$ and continuity of solution at $s = 0$. It may be shown from a consideration of the asymptotic form of (3.19) that an exponentially decaying solution does exist, but this will be omitted here since a more complete mathematical treatment of the inertial flow is to be presented in §4 (see equation (4.16)). The relevance of the similarity transformation to the general argument is that the asymptotic approach to the interior solution will be along lines of constant s rather than constant X. From (3.18) and an analogous poleward-directed transformation it may be seen how the mid-latitude jet will broaden to the east as it loses mass on the equatorward side, and how it will narrow to the east on the poleward side as it gains mass. This structure has been incorporated into the sketch presented in figure 4.

3.3. *The integrated vorticity constraint and the necessity for diffusive transfer*

We have up to this point discussed features of the general ocean circulation for which the model described by equation (3.1) is appropriate, i.e. the nature of the flow in the quasi-geostrophic region covering the major oceanic areas and the position and relative strength of the intense streams of high relative vorticity necessary to complete the flow field. There are, however, features of the circulation which cannot be deduced by such a simple model. For example, the values of $P^{\pm}$, or the amount of recirculation in each half-basin, are not determinate. Furthermore, the velocity distribution of the inertial solution discussed contains features which cannot occur in any real fluid; in each inertial boundary current, the velocity tangential to the coast reaches a maximum at the coast, and in the mid-latitude jet there is a discontinuity of tangential velocity across the zero-streamline. Any viscosity, no matter how small, must certainly smooth these discontinuities. If the (turbulent) viscosity is so small that this is the only role it plays in the general circulation, then viscous phenomena are essentially uninteresting from the large-scale point of view. We shall see, however, that this is not the case, by considering the constraint imposed upon the fluid motion by integrating the vorticity equation over the entire area of the ocean basin.

To perform the integration we note that the inertial terms may be rewritten, with the notation

$$\Delta = \partial^2/\partial\xi^2 + \lambda^2\,\partial^2/\partial\eta^2,$$

as

$$\psi_\xi \Delta\psi_\eta - \psi_\eta \Delta\psi_\xi = \partial(\psi\Delta\psi_\eta)/\partial\xi - \partial(\psi\Delta\psi_\xi)/\partial\eta; \tag{3.20}$$

we then multiply (3.1) by $d\xi\, d\eta$ and integrate over the range $(0, 1)$ in both variables to give

$$\epsilon\int_0^1 d\eta[\psi(\Delta\psi_\eta)_\eta]_{\xi=0}^{1} - \epsilon\int_0^1 d\xi[\psi(\Delta\psi_\xi)]_{\eta=0}^{1} + \int_0^1 d\eta\,\psi_{\xi=0}^{1} + \int_0^1\int_0^1 d\xi\, d\eta\, g(\eta) = 0 \tag{3.21}$$

or, since $\psi = 0$ on all boundaries, all terms vanish but the last, and (3.21) reduces to $\int_0^1 d\eta\, g(\eta) = 0$. But this is clearly impossible as $g(\eta)$ is positive definite, the wind-stress curl being everywhere of one sign over the ocean basin. Thus a completely inertial model violates the integrated vorticity constraint. The integration (3.21) is an explicit statement, in terms of the specific inertial model adopted here, of general objections which have been raised against complete inertial models on the grounds that integral conservation laws must be violated. It should be noted that (3.21) is an integral vorticity statement, and not an integral angular momentum statement, which need not be violated inertially (Morgan 1956, § 2).

The fact that the inertial model cannot satisfy the integrated constraint does not, of course, mean that the model is inadequate to describe those aspects of the flow to which it is applicable. Equation (3.1) must be regarded as an approximate form of the more complete equation (2.4). It provides for a local balance between a distributed source of vorticity (the integrated wind-stress curl) and the divergence of an advective flux of absolute vorticity, $\nabla^2\Psi + f$. However, the distributed vorticity source is everywhere of one sign and correspondingly there is a net input of vorticity into the fluid by the wind-stress. The vorticity advection, although balancing the source locally, can only redistribute vorticity internally, it cannot absorb vorticity. The only possible sink of vorticity is a diffusion into the boundaries.† The diffusive transfer process must, therefore, be included if the integrated balance is to be considered.

The inertial theory must therefore be regarded only as the inviscid core of a velocity field which also contains thin frictional layers, and when thus completed, will contain no physical paradoxes. In the limit of very small (horizontal) friction, which appears empirically to be the correct limit for the general ocean circulation, the flow field outside the frictional regions is determined essentially independently of friction. Mathematically, there is a three-scale problem, and the narrowest boundary-layer contribution (frictional scale) can fit on to whatever is required by the mutually-determined solutions from the two broader scales (quasi-geostrophic or geometric and inertial). Physically, however, the effects of friction on the general circulation is of great interest, since the ocean is a turbulent system which generates its own 'friction' and in which there is present only the minimum amount of turbulent diffusion necessary to satisfy overall conservation laws. In a sense the mean flow has control over the turbulence, rather than the turbulence controlling the mean flow. This is true in the region of the mid-latitude jet. In the region of the coasts the nature of the diffusive boundary layer is such that it contributes to the overall vorticity balance in a manner independent of the amount of friction present. To illustrate these ideas, we shall at this point introduce a process of diffusion by means of a constant coefficient of kinematic eddy viscosity, ν. We shall allow the eddy viscosity to have different constant values in the different regions where diffusion contributes to the local vorticity balance. In no sense do we imply that this approaches an accurate description of the turbulence. It does, however, provide a semi-quantitative description of the relation of diffusive transport to the other mechanisms of vorticity transfer which are present.

Thus we add to the vorticity equation a term $-\nu\Delta^4\Psi$, or in non-dimensional form, we replace equation (3.1) by

$$-\gamma\Delta\Delta\psi+\epsilon(\psi_\xi\Delta\psi_\eta-\psi_\eta\Delta\psi_\xi)+\psi_\xi+g(\eta)=0, \tag{3.22}$$

where $\gamma=\nu b/2\Omega\beta a^3$ is obviously related to a transport Ekman or Taylor number. We may immediately obtain relationships between γ and ϵ for the inertial currents discussed in §§3.1 and 3.2 to be a valid approximation to the flow, i.e. obtain bounds on the eddy viscosity in coastal and mid-latitude regions. Near a coast, $\partial/\partial\xi=O(\epsilon^{-\frac{1}{2}})$, and in the free jet, $\partial/\partial\eta=O(\epsilon^{-\frac{1}{3}})$. The sizes of the largest diffusive terms relative to the important advective terms are $\gamma\epsilon^{-\frac{3}{2}}$ and $\gamma\epsilon^{-\frac{4}{3}}$ respectively. Thus,

in a meridional inertial current:

$$\gamma<\epsilon^{\frac{3}{2}} \quad \text{or} \quad \nu<(\tau_0 ah^{-1})^{-\frac{3}{2}}b^{-1}(2\Omega\beta)^{-2}, \tag{3.23a}$$

in a latitudinal inertial current:

$$\gamma<\epsilon^{\frac{4}{3}}\lambda^{-2} \quad \text{or} \quad \nu<(\tau_0 h^{-1})^{\frac{4}{3}}a^{\frac{11}{3}}b^{-3}(2\Omega\beta)^{-\frac{5}{3}}. \tag{3.23b}$$

† We shall consider below only the possibility of diffusion into lateral boundaries, although it is conceivable that some vorticity may be diffused into the ocean bottom via barotropic eddies.

The simplest way to illustrate the nature of coastal frictional regions is to regard them from the point of view of boundary layers on the inertial current. Consequently, we introduce the inertial-layer variable, ζ_E or ξ_W, and add the diffusive term to equation (3.3), retaining only the term $\partial^4/\partial\xi^4$ in Δ. Thus

$$-\Gamma\psi_{\zeta\zeta\zeta\zeta}+\psi_\zeta\psi_{\zeta\zeta\eta}-\psi_\eta\psi_{\zeta\zeta\zeta}+\psi_\zeta = 0, \tag{3.24}$$

where $\Gamma = \gamma\epsilon^{-\frac{3}{2}}$ measures the effect of friction, and may be seen to be simply an inverse Reynolds number based on the eddy viscosity, the transport velocity at the quasi-geostrophic edge of the inertial layer, and the width of the inertial layer as a length scale. For large Reynolds number, frictional effects will be confined near the boundary $\zeta = 0$ and we introduce a scaled variable $\mu = \Gamma^r\zeta$ for this region.† The amplitude of the stream function must also be scaled in Γ; let $\psi = \Gamma^s\chi(\mu, \eta)$, where χ is a smooth function. The additional requirement is that the amplitude of the velocity parallel to the coast be the same in the frictional layer, where it is to be brought down to zero, as it is in the inertial layer, i.e. $\psi\zeta = \Gamma^{s+r}\chi\mu$ must remain independent of Γ, or $s = -r$. We then find that

$$\mu = \Gamma^{-\frac{1}{2}}\zeta, \quad \chi = \Gamma^{\frac{1}{2}}\psi, \tag{3.25}$$

and the approximate equation becomes

$$-\chi_{\mu\mu\mu\mu}+\chi_\mu\chi_{\mu\mu\eta}-\chi_\eta\chi_{\mu\mu\mu} = 0, \tag{3.26}$$

the equation for an ordinary non-rotating fluid boundary layer in which viscosity and inertia are balanced. This is seen to occur when the velocity normal to the coast, which is $O(1)$ in the quasi-geostrophic interior, is $O(\Gamma^{\frac{1}{2}})$.

For the integrated vorticity balance, we must replace (3.21) by the integral of (3.22) over the ocean basin. To evaluate the term $\Delta\Delta\psi$ we note that the contribution will be negligible except in coastal frictional boundary layers where the full term may be replaced approximately by $\psi_{\xi\xi\xi\xi}$. Thus the balance

$$\gamma\int_0^1 [\psi_{\xi\xi\xi}(0,\eta)-\psi_{\xi\xi\xi}(1,\eta)]\,d\eta+\int_0^1 g(\eta)\,d\eta = 0 \tag{3.27}$$

obtains. We note first that (3.26) is entirely independent of the eddy viscosity. This occurs because at the boundaries, from (3.25), we have that $\psi \sim \nu^{\frac{1}{3}}$, $\partial/\partial\xi \sim \nu^{-\frac{1}{3}}$. Since $\gamma \sim \nu$, the combination $\gamma\psi_{\xi\xi\xi}$ does not contain ν. As the eddy viscosity becomes smaller, the gradients sharpen in the viscous layer in such a manner as always to maintain the integrated vorticity constraint. Furthermore, we can obtain the value of $\psi_{\xi\xi\xi}$ on the coasts, explicitly in terms of the quasi-geostrophic interior solutions, by integrating once the full boundary-layer equation (3.24). The integral may be performed simply by rewriting the inertial terms as

$$\psi_\zeta\psi_{\zeta\zeta\eta}-\psi_\eta\psi_{\zeta\zeta\zeta} = \partial(\psi_\zeta\psi_{\zeta\eta}-\psi_\eta\psi_{\zeta\zeta})/\partial\zeta.$$

Since on the coasts in the presence of friction $\psi_\zeta = \psi_\eta = 0$, and interior to the inertial currents the relative vorticity is negligible, these terms yield nothing when integrated across the frictional and inertial boundary layers, from the coast to the quasi-geostrophic interior. From (3.5), (3.24) and (3.25),

$$\gamma\psi_{\xi\xi\xi}(0,\eta) = -g(\eta)P, \quad \gamma\psi_{\xi\xi\xi}(1,\eta) = -g(\eta)(P-1), \tag{3.28a, b}$$

and in virtue of the restrictions $P^+ > 1$, $P^- < 0$, it is seen from (3.27) that the equatorward-western and poleward-eastern boundaries diffuse into the ocean

† See note added in proof stage at end of paper.

vorticity of opposite sign to that of the distributed wind source, while the equatorward-eastern and poleward-western boundaries diffuse vorticity of the same sign as the wind.

Equations (3.28*a*, *b*) provide expressions for the diffusive contributions to (3.27) valid everywhere on the western and eastern coasts except for a narrow latitude belt of width $\epsilon^{\frac{1}{4}}$ situated about the centre of the mid-latitude jet, or at the latitude of maximum wind-stress curl. If the contributions from these short stretches of the coasts be neglected, which seems *a priori* reasonable, (3.27) may be evaluated. Under the assumption of a wind-stress curl which is symmetric about the middle latitude $\eta = \frac{1}{2}$, e.g. (2.8), the vorticity integral (3.27) becomes simply

$$\tfrac{1}{2}\{-P^{+}-P^{-}+(P^{+}-1)+(P^{-}-1)\}+1 = 0, \qquad (3.29)$$

which is seen to be automatically satisfied for any amounts of recirculation in the two half-basins. There is, however, another point of view which is physically more plausible than that adopted here for the evaluation of (3.27), and which yields a minimum lower bound on P^{+} which is higher than that obtained from inertial considerations alone. The detailed argument will be reserved for §4 and only an outline presented here. The physical basis is the diffusion of vorticity in the region of the mid-latitude jet.

As has been mentioned above, diffusion must certainly act to eliminate the tangential velocity discontinuity at the mid-latitude zero-streamlines. That diffusion do no more than this at mid-latitudes is the basis for the inequality (3.23*b*), under which a very narrow frictional region will be sandwiched between two inertial streams. That this cannot be the case can be seen by considering integrated vorticity constraints for partial areas of the ocean basin, e.g. in the lower half-basin, over the three frictional sub-layers (lying along $\xi = 0$, 1, $\eta = \frac{1}{2}$) on the one hand and over the quasi-geostrophic pulse inertial current regions on the other hand. Each such region will be found to be separately out of balance, the vorticity diffused out of the ocean at the boundaries not having been allowed to diffuse out of the body of the fluid into which it was put by the distributed source.† It is plausible to assume that this occurs in the region of the mid-latitude jet, since boundary currents are known to be essentially inertial. If this be the case, the inequality (3.21*b*) must at least become an equality; hence $\nu = 10^{7}\,\mathrm{cm^2/sec}$ (evaluated for numbers typical of the North Atlantic). Thus the theory of the mean flow yields a crude but quantitative prediction of the amount of turbulence which must be present. A simple dimensional argument from the largest-scale meanders of the Gulf Stream after it leaves the coast at Cape Hatteras gives $\nu = 10^{8}\,\mathrm{cm^2/sec}$ as a crude empirical estimate of the eddy viscosity in this region.

Furthermore, under the assumption that diffusion does occur in the region of the mid-latitude current in a wide enough region to destroy the purely inertial character of the jet, it is highly unlikely that only a minimum of vorticity will be diffused. Consider therefore the possibility that the vorticity advected into

† From a formal point of view we may say that every streamline of the flow must go through a frictional region, since inertial currents conserve (potential) vorticity along streamlines.

the narrow core of the jet from the western walls has essentially all diffused and broadened the jet as it reaches the eastern wall. Assuming the separation of the eastern coastal currents into inertial and frictional regions to be maintained, it may be inferred that there can be no net diffusion of vorticity into the ocean along the eastern coast. In such a case the vorticity diffusion along the short stretch of eastern coast around the mid-latitude is not negligible; in fact, it cancels the contribution (3.28). As will be argued in §4, from the nature of better understood but similar stagnation points of fluid, flow, it is possible for this to occur while the corresponding contribution from the western coast does remain negligible. In this extreme case, we replace (3.29) by a relationship containing no eastern coast contribution,

$$\tfrac{1}{2}(-P^{+}-P^{-})+1 = 0, \quad \text{or} \quad P^{+} = 2-P^{-}, \tag{3.30}$$

and, since $P^{-} \leqslant 0$, the minimum value of $P^{+} = 2$. In this case the transport of the equatorward-western current (Gulf Stream or Kuroshio) is twice that given by the purely frictional theory, and all the vorticity input by the wind is balanced by diffusion in this region. In a less extreme case, the vorticity balance in the eastern coastal currents could be partially maintained by a breakdown of the strict separation into purely inertial and frictional streams. The transports of the Gulf Stream and Kuroshio would then be more than, but less than twice, that given by the Sverdrup–Munk value. Furthermore, this would yield eastern currents which are broader and less well defined than western currents, which is apparently the case observationally. This view may be supported by the fact that the eastern currents have a downstream mass efflux, and would tend to be more unstable than their western counterparts.

An interesting consequence of this discussion is that in each half-basin a balance does not obtain between wind-stress curl and coastal diffusion of vorticity. A balance is maintained only by a meridional transport of vorticity by the meanders or eddies in the mid-latitude jet. If it can be shown that these meanders do indeed effect a transfer of vorticity between low and high latitudes, then they play, in the general circulation of the ocean, the same vital role that large scale meanders in the jet stream are known to play in the general circulation of the atmosphere.

In the following sections we shall develop the inertial flows with additional generality and then present further arguments as to the implication of turbulent diffusion.

4. The inertial boundary-layer theory

We return now to discuss, for a more general geometry and wind-stress distribution, the model described in §2.

The differential equation (3.1) for the transport stream function ψ is

$$\psi_{\xi}(\epsilon\Delta\psi+f)_{\eta}-\psi_{\eta}(\epsilon\Delta\psi+f)_{\xi}+g(\eta) = 0, \tag{4.1}$$

where $f(\eta)$ is a redefined non-dimensional form of the latitudinally varying vertical component of the earth's rotation. The boundaries lie at $\xi = \xi_1(\eta)$, $\xi = \xi_2(\eta)$, $\eta = 0$ and $\eta = L$. The former of these are continental barriers on which ψ must vanish and the latter are those latitudes at which $g(\eta)$, the curl of the wind stress, vanishes. We shall see that ψ may also be taken to vanish at these latitudes. The number L determines the length scaling (the quantity b of equation (3.1) times L is the distance from $\eta = 0$ to $\eta = L$), and we use the same scale in the longitudinal direction so that $a = b$ and $\lambda = 1$ (a, b, λ are quantities introduced with equation (3.1)).

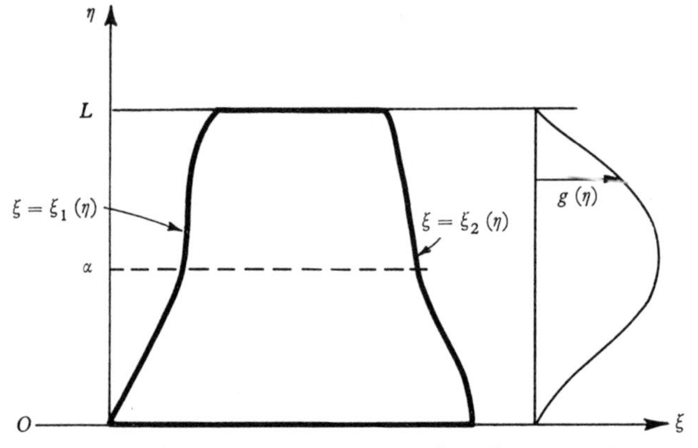

FIGURE 5. Geometry of ocean basin and wind-stress curl $g(\eta)$.

Both because of the mathematical structure of the problem [i.e. because the most highly differentiated terms in (4.1) have a very small coefficient (Carrier 1953)] and because of the foregoing discussion, we anticipate that the circulation pattern will display a boundary-layer structure and that ψ can be written in the form

$$\psi(\xi, \eta) = \psi^{(0)}(\xi, \eta) + \psi^{(1)}(\zeta_1, \eta) + \psi^{(2)}(\zeta_2, \eta), \tag{4.2}$$

where $\zeta_j = [\xi - \xi_j(\eta)]\, \epsilon^{-\frac{1}{2}}$. In choosing this representation for ψ, we deliberately do *not* allow sufficient generality because we wish to *deduce* the necessity of a more highly subdivided structure. We shall find, in fact, that the interior domain must be divided into two regions (as in §3) and that inertial currents (boundary layers) will occupy not only the eastern and western boundaries, but that an intense current will also flow at constant latitude across the ocean basin at $\eta = \alpha$, the latitude of maximum wind-stress curl.

Since $\psi^{(1)}$ and $\psi^{(2)}$ describe boundary layers, they must die out exponentially as $\zeta_1 \to \infty$, $\zeta_2 \to -\infty$, respectively.

We substitute (4.2) into (4.1) and segregate into three groups the various contributions which emerge, to give

$$\begin{aligned}
&[\psi^{(0)}_{\xi} f'(\eta) + g(\eta) + O(\epsilon^{\frac{1}{2}})] \\
&\quad + \epsilon^{-\frac{1}{2}}[(\psi^{(1)}_{\zeta_1} \psi^{(1)}_{\zeta_1\zeta_1\eta} - \psi^{(1)}_{\eta} \psi^{(1)}_{\zeta_1\zeta_1\zeta_1})\, q_1(\eta) - \psi^{(0)}_{s1}(\eta)\, \psi^{(1)}_{\zeta_1\zeta_1\zeta_1} + \psi^{(1)}_{\zeta_1} f'(\eta) + O(\epsilon^{\frac{1}{2}})] \\
&\quad + \epsilon^{-\frac{1}{2}}[(\psi^{(2)}_{\zeta_2} \psi^{(2)}_{\zeta_2\zeta_2\eta} - \psi^{(2)}_{\eta} \psi^{(2)}_{\zeta_2\zeta_2\zeta_2})\, q_2(\eta) - \psi^{(0)}_{s2}\, \psi^{(2)}_{\zeta_2\zeta_2\zeta_2} + \psi^{(2)}_{\zeta_2} f'(\eta) + O(\epsilon^{\frac{1}{2}})] = 0.
\end{aligned} \tag{4.3}$$

The first bracket contains all terms which are not exponentially small far from the lateral boundaries; the second contains those terms which are not small near the western boundary; the third contains the terms which determine the structure of the eastern boundary layer; the quantities q_j and ψ_{sj} appearing in (4.3) are $1+[\xi_j'(\eta)]^2$ and the directional derivative of $\psi^{(0)}$ along the boundary $\xi = \xi_j(\eta)$, respectively. Equation (4.1) and this discussion imply that

$$\psi_\xi^{(0)} f'(\eta) = g(\eta) = 0, \tag{4.4}$$

and, hence, that

$$\psi^{(0)} = g(\eta)\,[a(\eta)-\xi]/f'(\eta), \tag{4.5}$$

where $a(\eta)$ has yet to be determined.†

The second bracket of (4.3) must also vanish and so

$$(\psi_{\zeta_1}^{(1)}\psi_{\zeta_1\zeta_1\eta}^{(1)} - \psi_\eta^{(1)}\psi_{\zeta_1\zeta_1\zeta_1}^{(1)})\,q_1(\eta) - \psi_{s1}^{(0)}(\eta)\,\psi_{\zeta_1\zeta_1\zeta_1}^{(1)} + \psi_{\zeta_1}^{(1)} f'(\eta) = 0. \tag{4.6}$$

The treatment of this equation is simplified by writing

$$\psi_{\zeta_1\zeta_1}^{(1)} = F[\psi^{(1)}, \eta], \tag{4.7}$$

whereupon (4.6) becomes

$$\psi_{\zeta_1}^{(1)}\,[q_1 F_\eta - \psi_{s1}^{(0)}(\eta)\,F_{\psi^{(1)}} + f'(\eta)] = 0. \tag{4.8}$$

It follows that

$$F(\psi^{(1)}, \eta) = -W_1(\eta) + G_1[\psi^{(1)} + \chi_1(\eta)], \tag{4.9}$$

where

$$W_1(\eta) = \int_0^\eta \frac{f'(\eta)}{q_1(\eta)}\,d\eta, \quad \chi_1(\eta) = \int_0^\eta \frac{\psi_{s1}^{(0)}(\eta)}{q_1(\eta)}\,d\eta,$$

and (thus far) $G_1(u)$ is any differentiable function of u. However, if $\psi^{(1)}$, the solution of (4.7), is to die out as $\zeta_1 \to \infty$, $F(0, \eta)$ must be zero. Thus

$$G_1[\chi_1(\eta)] = W_1(\eta). \tag{4.10}$$

If we define $\eta_1^*(\chi_1)$ to be the inverse of $\chi_1(\eta)$, then

$$G_1(u) = W_1[\eta_1^*(u)]. \tag{4.11}$$

In order to see simply the implications of (4.11) which are vital to the determination of the current structure, it is convenient to consider a simple but realistic example. Let $L = \pi$, $\xi_1(\eta) = 0$, $\xi_2(\eta) = \text{const.} = \xi_2$, $g(\eta) = \sin\eta$, $f = f_0 + \eta$. This $g(\eta)$ is a reasonable qualitative approximation to the observed wind-stress curl over the major ocean basins, and the slowly varying trigometric form of the correct $f(\eta)$ is approximated by η, as is customary on a β-plane model. With these definitions,

$$W_1(\eta) = \eta, \quad \chi_1(\eta) = \psi_\eta^{(0)}(0, \eta) = A_1 \sin\eta,$$

and we arbitrarily take $a(\eta)$ to be the constant $A_1 > 0$; we defer until later a more comprehensive discussion of this choice. Thus $G_1(u) = \sin^{-1}(u/A_1)$, so that

$$F(\psi^{(1)}, \eta) = -\eta + \sin^{-1}\{A_1^{-1}[\psi^{(1)}(\zeta_1, \eta) + \psi^{(0)}(\eta, 0)]\}, \tag{4.12}$$

and

$$\psi_{\zeta_1\zeta_1}^{(1)} = -\eta + \sin^{-1}\{A_1^{-1}[\psi^{(1)}(\zeta_1, \eta) + \psi^{(0)}(\eta, 0)]\}. \tag{4.13}$$

Equation (4.13) can be integrated explicitly by quadratures. In particular, multiplication by ψ_{ζ_1} and integration over ζ_1 yields

$$[\psi_{\zeta_1}^{(1)}(\zeta, \eta)]^2 - [\psi_{\zeta_1}^{(1)}(0, \eta)]^2 + 2\eta[\psi^{(1)}(\zeta_1, \eta) - \psi^{(1)}(0, \eta)] = 2A[u\sin^{-1}u + (1-u^2)^{\frac{1}{2}} - 1],$$

where $u = \sin\eta + A_1^{-1}\psi^{(1)}(\zeta, \eta)$.

† Note that the choice of $\psi^{(0)}$ in this form, with $a(\eta)$ bounded in $0 \leqslant \eta \leqslant 1$, implies that $\psi^{(0)}(\xi, 0) = \psi^{(0)}(\xi, L) = 0$. Thus $\eta = 0$ and $\eta = L$ are streamlines of flow. We limit ourselves, in this investigation, to such $\psi^{(0)}$ but we note in doing so that no other choice of $\psi^{(0)}$ permits the elimination of any of the inertial currents which are obtained in the following.

Since

$$\psi^{(1)}(\infty,\eta) = 0 \quad \text{and} \quad \psi^{(1)}(0,\eta) = -\psi^{(0)}(0,\eta), \quad [\psi^{(1)}_{\zeta_1}(0,\eta)]^2 = 2A_1(1-\cos\eta).$$

Thus, at $\eta = \frac{1}{2}\pi$, the velocity at the continental barrier is proportional to $A_1^{\frac{1}{2}}$.

Using (4.13), when $\eta < \frac{1}{2}\pi$ and we define $\sin^{-1}(0) = 0$, $\psi^{(1)}_{\zeta_1\zeta_1}(0,\eta) < 0$, and, as $\zeta_1 \to \infty$, $\psi^{(1)}_{\zeta_1\zeta_1} \to 0$. However, when $\eta > \frac{1}{2}\pi$, $\sin^{-1}\{A_1^{-1}[\psi^{(1)}+\psi^{(0)}]\}$ begins with the value zero at $\zeta_1 = 0$ and tends to $\pi-\eta$ as $\psi^{(1)} \to 0$, thus making it impossible for $\psi^{(1)}_{\zeta_1\zeta_1}$ to vanish. In other words, equation (4.13) has no solution which approaches zero as $\zeta_1 \to \infty$. *Thus the inertial boundary layer on the western side of the ocean can continue poleward only up to the latitude where $g(\eta)$ has its maximum value.* For more general $f(\eta)$, $g(\eta)$, $\xi_1(\eta)$, the greatest poleward penetration of the western current cannot exceed $\eta = \alpha$, the latitude at which $[A(\eta)-\xi_1(\eta)]\,g(\eta)/f'(\eta)$ has its maximum value.

The equations which govern the behaviour of the eastern current are identical with those for $\psi^{(1)}$ except that the index 2 replaces the index 1. The solution $\psi^{(2)}$ of that equation will die out as $\zeta_2 \to -\infty$ provided $a(\eta)-\xi_2(\eta) > 0$; $\psi^{(2)}$ can be found by integrating (4.13).

Once again, by identical arguments, the current (which flows towards the equator) can be continued only as far poleward as that latitude where $[a(\eta)-\xi_2(\eta)]\,g(\eta)/f'(\eta)$ has its maximum. Mass conservation in the large can now be included in the theory only if a current flows eastward from the poleward terminus of the western current to that of the eastern current. This current can be sought as still another boundary layer using the description

$$\psi = \psi^{(0)}+\psi^{(1)}+\psi^{(2)}+\psi^{(3)}(\xi,\sigma),$$

where $\sigma = \epsilon^{-\frac{1}{3}}[\eta-\alpha]$.

With this modification of ψ, equation (4.3) will be modified by the addition of another bracket, which must vanish independently of the other brackets of that equation. Thus

$$\psi^{(3)}_{\xi}\psi^{(3)}_{\eta\eta\eta} - \psi^{(3)}_{\eta}\psi^{(3)}_{\eta\eta\xi} + \psi^{(0)}_{\xi}(\xi,\alpha)\,\psi^{(3)}_{\eta\eta\eta} + f'(\alpha) = 0. \tag{4.14}$$

This equation admits a similarity solution of the form

$$\psi^{(3)} = \{a(\alpha)-\xi\}\,h[\sigma\{a(\alpha)-\xi\}^{-\frac{1}{3}}] = [a(\alpha)-\xi]\,h(\tau). \tag{4.15}$$

Substitution of this representation of $\psi^{(3)}$ into (4.14) yields the equation

$$(1+h)\,h''' - \tfrac{1}{3}h'h'' + h - \tfrac{1}{3}\tau h' + O(\epsilon^{\frac{1}{3}}) = 0.$$

The relevant solution of this equation is one whose asymptotic behaviour for large negative τ (as governed by the linear terms of (4.15)) is

$$h_1 \sim C\tau^{-\frac{1}{4}}\exp\,(2\tau^{\frac{3}{2}}/3\sqrt{3}), \tag{4.16}$$

and for which $h_1(0) = g(\alpha)/f'(\alpha)$. The details of h_1 can be found by numerical integration but, once again, such details provide no particular advantage.

The description of the flow for $\eta < \alpha$ which is provided by $\psi_0+\psi_1+\psi_2+\psi_3$ is unsatisfactory only in the poleward corners where the boundary layers join. The efflux of vorticity from the western current defined by $\psi^{(1)}(\zeta_1, \alpha)$ differs markedly from that entering the horizontal current described by $\psi^{(3)}(0, \sigma)$ and a similar situation prevails near the point $[\xi_2(\alpha), \alpha]$. The former is of order unity and the latter of order $\epsilon^{\frac{1}{3}}$. Before resolving this difficulty by invoking frictional considerations, we must discuss the flow above $\eta = \alpha$.

The analysis proceeds precisely as before; we denote the stream function by ϕ instead of ψ and use $\phi^{(0)}$, $\phi^{(1)}$, $\phi^{(2)}$, $\phi^{(3)}$, respectively, to describe the interior flow and the western, eastern and central inertial currents. The independent variables ζ_1, ζ_2, σ are defined precisely as before; in fact,

$$\phi^{(0)}(\xi, \eta) = [a^*(\eta) - \xi]\, g(\eta)/f'(\eta). \tag{4.17}$$

$\phi^{(1)}(\xi, \eta)$ is the solution of $\phi^{(1)}_{\zeta_1\zeta_1} = F(\phi^{(1)}, \eta)$ and

$$q_1 F_\eta - \phi^{(0)}_{s1}(\eta)\, F_{\phi^{(1)}} + f'(\eta) = 0. \tag{4.18}$$

It follows that

$$F(\phi^{(1)}, \eta) = -W(\eta) + G[\phi^{(1)} + \chi_1(\eta)], \tag{4.19}$$

where

$$W = \int_0^\eta \frac{f'(\eta)}{q_1(\eta)}\, d\eta, \quad \chi_1(\eta) = -\int_0^\eta \frac{\phi^{(0)}_{s1}(\eta)}{q_1(\eta)}\, d\eta,$$

and that $G(u)$ is defined in terms of η^{**} the inverse of $\psi^{(0)}_{s1}(\eta)$ by the relation

$$G(u) = W[\eta^{**}(u)]. \tag{4.20}$$

For the special case treated before, $W(\eta) = \eta$ and $G(u) = \sin^{-1}(u/B_1)$, where we now take $a^*(\eta) = B_1$ in the description of $\phi^{(0)}$, and we must now define $\sin^{-1}(0) = \pi$. However, with these definitions of W and G, the number B_1 must be negative if the solution of (4.17) for $\eta > \frac{1}{2}\pi$ is to die out as $\zeta_1 \to \infty$. In the general case, instead of $B_1 \leqslant 0$, we have $a^*(\eta) - \xi_1(\eta) \leqslant 0$, in $\eta \geqslant \alpha$. The eastern boundary current in $\eta > \alpha$ can be treated in precisely the same way and the only new requirement, $a^*(\eta) - \xi_2(\eta) \leqslant 0$, is already implied by (4.18). Similarly, the boundary layer just above $\eta = \alpha$ provides no new criteria.

At this stage, then, we find a family of flow descriptions which has discrepancies in vorticity transport in the corners near $\{\xi_1(\alpha), \alpha\}$, and near $\{\xi_2(\alpha), \alpha\}$. The lack of uniqueness is contained in the function $a(\eta)$ [which is restricted only in that $a(\eta) \geqslant \xi_2(\eta)$ for $\eta < \alpha$] and the function $a^*(\eta)$ [which must only obey the inequality $a^*(\eta) \leqslant \xi_1(\eta)$ for $\eta > \alpha$].

This lack of uniqueness cannot be removed in a purely inertial theory and we must invoke further considerations to partially resolve the difficulties.

5. The effects of turbulent diffusion

It was noted in § 3.3 that the integral of the left side of equation (4.1) over the domain cannot be zero. $g(\eta)$ is a positive function over that domain and the other terms provide a vanishing contribution. It is not surprising, then, that there should be discrepancies in the vorticity transport. One can attempt to resolve this difficulty in either of two ways. The first of these is to replace (4.1) by an equation in which the frictional effects are modelled in some specific way and then solve that equation. If the friction were introduced by a pseudo-laminar model with an eddy viscosity appropriate to the turbulent state of the fluid, equation (4.1) would be replaced by

$$\gamma\Delta\Delta\psi + \psi_\xi(\epsilon\Delta\psi + f)_\eta - \psi_\eta(\epsilon\Delta\psi + f)_\xi + g(\eta) = 0, \tag{5.1}$$

where γ has been defined following equation (3.20). This equation could be solved for very small γ, an appropriate choice since our present knowledge of turbulent transport in the oceans indicates that $\gamma \ll \epsilon$ in the continental boundary regions.

In doing so, we would regard the results of the inertial theory of §4 as the description of the interior flow of a new boundary-layer problem, in which the viscous terms then provide the mechanism for additional boundary layers along the continental barriers. These frictional boundary layers are much thinner than the inertial layers they adjoin. The detailed solution is of little interest since this friction model is of questionable validity; fortunately, it is also unnecessary. Once we are convinced of the existence of a frictional boundary layer of thickness $\delta \ll \epsilon^{\frac{1}{2}}$ along, say, the western boundary below $\eta = \alpha$, we can evaluate its con-

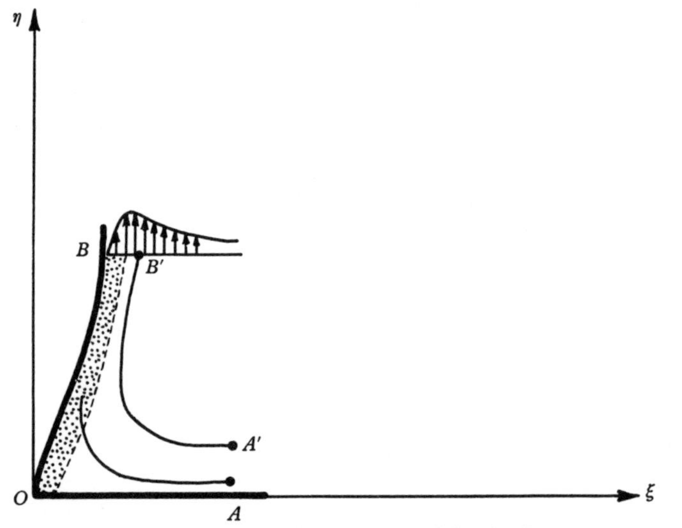

FIGURE 6. Western velocity distribution and friction-layer geometry.

tribution to the gross vorticity balance as follows. Figure 6 shows, schematically, the friction layer and a stream line, $A'B'$, lying entirely outside the friction layer, but near the landward edge of the inertial current.

The convection of vorticity across AA' is negligible in view of the very small velocity ψ_η in this region; the diffusion of vorticity across OA and across $A'B'$ are negligible because each of these streamlines does not lie in the friction layer. Thus, the diffusion of vorticity across OB must be equal to the efflux of vorticity across BB'. The latter quantity, E, is given by

$$E = \int_B^{B'} vv_x dx = \tfrac{1}{2}\{v^2(B') - v^2(B)\} = \tfrac{1}{2}v^2(B'). \tag{5.2}$$

We conclude that the vorticity contributed by diffusion across the barrier via the friction layer OB is equal to one-half the square of the inertial-theory velocity evaluated at the wall. This, as we showed in §4, is proportional to A_1. We see, by similar calculations, that the (counter-clockwise) vorticity diffused across the upper western boundary is B_1.

The following arguments indicate that negligible vorticity is diffused across the eastern boundary. Note that although the vorticity flux in the horizontal current may lie in a very slender ribbon of fluid at the western end, any such concentration of vorticity will diffuse broadly as the current proceeds towards the eastern boundary. Thus, a very small part of this vorticity will enter the eastern friction layers. Furthermore, little vorticity emerges from the eastern friction layers since the inertial current velocity at $\eta = 0$ and at $\eta = L$ is zero. Since this is a decelerating flow, these friction layers must be less well defined (more diffuse) than those on the western boundary. The vorticity balance corresponding to that illustrated in figure 6 for the western boundary is shown in figure 7. Since little vorticity crosses $D'C'CD$, no important vorticity contributions can diffuse across $D'E'ED$.

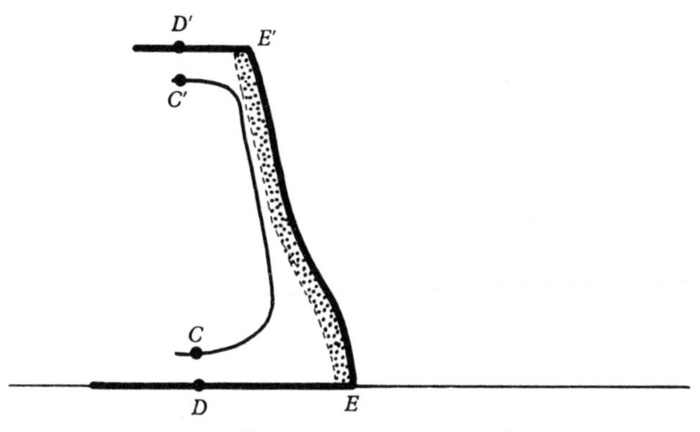

FIGURE 7. Eastern friction layer and geometry.

It follows (once the dimensional parameters have been included properly) that

$$A_1 + B_1 = \int_\Gamma g(\eta)\, d\eta\, d\xi, \tag{5.3}$$

where Γ is the domain defined following equation (4.1). Since $A_1 \geqslant 0$, $B_1 \leqslant 0$, the weakest possible circulation is that for which $B_1 = 0$ and

$$A_1 = \int g\, d\eta\, d\xi. \tag{5.4}$$

The degree of difficulty associated with the detailed integration of the foregoing equations depend markedly on the detailed description of $f(\eta)$, $g(\eta)$, $a(\eta)$, $a^*(\eta)$, etc. However, the conclusions are rather insensitive to such detail. If $g(\alpha)$ is unity and if $A_1 = a(\alpha)$, $B_1 = a^*(\alpha)$, the foregoing conclusions still hold. This theory, therefore, gives a lower bound on the circulation which is significantly greater than (by a factor of 2) and in much better agreement with the observations† than is the prediction of previously discussed models.

† That is, the observed transports as reported by Munk (1950, table 2). Since the transports are deduced from observed profiles of density under the assumption of a level of no meridional motion, care must be exercised in their interpretation. It is hoped to be able to remove partially this ambiguity by returning to the data with less restrictive assumptions (Stommel, private communication; see Stommel 1958, p. 164).

6. Discussion

The general consequences of the model can now be described. We consider any wind stress distribution† whose curl has a single maximum at latitude $\eta = \alpha$ and vanishes at the two latitudes $\eta = 0$ and $\eta = L > \alpha$. The basin geometry is that of figure 4. When we postulate that no flow crosses the latitude $\eta = 0, L$, in reasonable conformity with Northern hemisphere observations,‡ the flow over most of the basin [excluding the neighbourhood of $\xi = \xi_1(\eta)$, $\xi = \xi_2(\eta), \eta = \alpha$] is given by equations (4.5) and (4.17). *These descriptions are not unique and cannot be made so without detailed solution of a dissipative model.* However, the constraints imposed by gross dissipative considerations are already very informative.

The intensive flow near $\xi = \xi_1(\eta)$ and $\xi = \xi_2(\eta)$ can be expected to be of boundary-layer type, but these boundary layers cannot be continued from $\eta < \alpha$ into $\eta > a$. It follows from the disjoint character of the layer along ξ_1 (for example) that another intensive current must move eastward from the point $[\xi_1(\alpha), \alpha]$. Note that these inertial boundary currents provide constraints on the general flow described by (4.5) and (4.17), which have the form $a(\eta) > \xi_2(\eta)$ in $\eta < \alpha, a^*(\eta) < \xi_1(\eta)$ in $\eta > \alpha$. The gross vorticity balance further restricts the choice of $a(\eta)$ and $a^*(\eta)$ by demanding that

$$a(\alpha) + a^*(\alpha) = \int g(\eta)\, d\eta\, d\xi.$$

Since $a^* \leqslant \xi_1(\eta)$, the smallest value for $a(\alpha)$ is given by

$$a(\alpha) > \int g(\eta)\, d\xi\, d\eta - \xi_1(\alpha). \tag{6.1}$$

This provides a lower bound for $a(\alpha)$ which supersedes the foregoing constraints $a(\alpha) \geqslant \xi_2(\alpha)$.

Using, now, any $a(\eta)$ and $a^*(\eta)$ which obey the foregoing constraints, we find in the region $\eta < \alpha$ that V, the net vorticity input from $g(\eta)$ and from solid boundaries, is not zero but negative and that the input in the region $\eta > \alpha$ is $-V$.

The current along $\eta = \alpha$ must therefore accomplish two things. It must transfer from the upper half-basin into the lower half-basin all of the vorticity which diffused into the stream along $\xi = \xi_1(\eta)$, $\eta > \alpha$ and that which was put in by the wind-stress curl, $g(\eta)$. It must also change the distribution of vorticity among streamlines in such a way that fluid enters the interior region of the lower basin with a vorticity commensurate with $\psi^{(0)}$. To do this, the width of the zone affected by friction (turbulent transfer) must be as wide as the inertial current.

† Despite the introduction of our model as an effort to understand primarily the circulation structure in the 15° to 55° N. latitude range, it is equally appropriate to the lower latitudes where similar but narrower latitude bands exist with wind-stress curl variations from zero to a maximum to zero. In these latitude bands, the complex subsurface current structure seems to be consistent with this analysis and the β-plane approximation ($f \simeq f + \beta\eta$) is a very good one indeed. (We are, of course, not referring to the Cromwell current.)

‡ The geometry is much more complicated in the Southern hemisphere and will be discussed elsewhere.

As a dominant process, we suggest the instability associated with the fact that the fluid enters the mid-latitude jet with velocities which are of order $\epsilon^{-\frac{1}{2}}$, instead of the $\epsilon^{-\frac{1}{3}}$ appropriate to such a stream;† the entering vorticity is correspondingly high. The deceleration process is certain to be violent and the transfer occurs. It is clear, however, that this argument as it stands is not adequate to provide a mechanistic description of the transfer process or a quantitative prediction of $a(\alpha)$.

The foregoing combination of an inviscid boundary-layer theory and a heuristic dissipation model gives a self-consistent description of ocean-basin flows which are in rather good agreement with Northern hemisphere observations and at least suggestive for the Southern hemisphere. In particular, the quantity $a(\alpha)$, which defines the transport, is required by this theory to be twice as large as that of previous theories. The minimum values acceptable within this theory are close to those of the real oceans.

In brief, then, we *deduce* the presence of the mid-latitude jet and an estimate of the circulation; we *infer* the gross character and location of the turbulent vorticity by merely noting the role of the diffusive processes which are required in order that they together with the clearly deduced flow form a coherent and self-consistent physical picture.

It is a pleasure to acknowledge the stimulation afforded by Professor Henry Stommel's continued interest. Thanks are due to the Office of Naval Research (GFC) and to the Research Corporation (ARR) for their support during the period of this research.

REFERENCES

Carrier, G. F. 1953 Boundary layer problems in applied mechanics. *Adv. Appl. Mech.* **3**, 1953.

Charney J. G. 1955 The Gulf Stream as an inertial boundary layer. *Proc. Nat. Acad. Sci. Wash.* **41**, 731.

Fofonoff, N. P. 1954 Steady flow in a frictionless homogeneous ocean. *J. Marine Res.* **13**, 254.

Morgan, G. W. 1956 On the wind-driven ocean circulation. *Tellus*, **8**, 301.

Munk, W. H. 1950 On the wind-driven ocean circulation. *J. Met.* **7**, 79.

Munk, W. H. & Carrier, G. F. 1950 The wind-driven circulation in ocean basins of various shapes. *Tellus*, **2**, 158.

Sverdrup, H. U. 1947 Wind-driven currents in a baroclinic ocean; with application to the equatorial currents of the eastern Pacific. *Proc. Nat. Acad. Sci. Wash.* **33**, 318.

Stommel, H. 1948 The westward intensification of wind-driven ocean currents. *Trans. Amer. Geophys. Un.* **29**, 202.

Stommel, H. 1955 Lateral eddy-viscosity in the Gulf Stream system. *Deep Sea Res.* **3**, 88.

Stommel, H. 1958 *The Gulf Stream: a Physical and Dynamical Description.* Cambridge University Press.

† More precisely, the fluid must enter the corner region with velocity of one amplitude and leave with velocity of another amplitude. The resulting instability may enlarge the transition region, which conceivably includes the whole region of maximum meandering.

Note added in proof

As was pointed out to the authors by Derek Moore, the reader could infer, in §3.3 and in §4, that one can construct by conventional laminar boundary-layer analysis a description of a frictional modification of the inertial flow pattern derived earlier. This is certainly correct in so far as the western boundary regions are concerned, but it is not true for the eastern boundaries. The decelerating character of the inviscid flow near the eastern boundaries implies that such conventional boundary layers cannot be constructed. This is disturbing only because one cannot state with assured accuracy the distance to which boundary-generated vorticity will migrate. It is unlikely that the general flow pattern will be modified appreciably by this difficulty, and especially unlikely that the circulation-estimating inequality (which is controlled by western boundary considerations) will be affected. In other words, a constant eddy coefficient as introduced is inappropriate for a discussion of the structure of the flow field, although it is useful for some order of magnitude estimates.

ADDENDUM

In the development of a description of the mid-latitude jet (p. 142) we anticipated that the stream function could be represented in that region by $\psi \simeq \psi^{(0)}(\xi, \eta) + \psi^{(3)}(\xi, \tau)$. A differential equation was derived for $\psi^{(3)}$ and the asymptotic behavior (equation 4.16) of an appropriate solution was quoted. This quotation contains a misprint; $\psi^{(3)}$ should be proportional to $\tau^{-9/4}$ not $\tau^{-1/4}$. This is irrelevant, however, since efforts to construct the appropriate solution numerically indicate clearly that no solution exists which has that asymptotic behavior and which also obeys the boundary conditions at $\tau = 0$. Accordingly, we must modify the description of ψ. We must anticipate, in fact, that the boundary layer is characterized, not by a single length scale, but by two such scales. That is, we seek ψ in the form

$$\psi \simeq \psi^{(0)}(\xi, \eta) + \psi^{(j)}[\xi, \epsilon^{j}(a - \eta)] + \psi^{(b)}[\xi, \epsilon^{-1/3}(a - \eta)].$$

Upon substitution of this representation into (4.14) one readily sees that no solution with $j < -1/3$ can be used, but that a solution with any j in the range $0 > j > -1/3$ is consistent. Since ψ^{j} is concerned with the mass recirculation phenomenon, the ambiguity in j is merely another aspect of this lack of uniqueness of the inviscid model. Thus

$$\psi \simeq \psi^{(0)}(\xi, \eta) - ag[\xi, \epsilon^{j}(a - \eta)] + \xi f(\tau),$$

where $\tau = \epsilon^{-1/3}(a - \eta)/\xi^{1/3}$, $0 > j > -1/3$, $g(\xi, 0) = 1$, $f(0) = 1$, and $(g_{\xi\xi} + g_{\eta\eta}) = F(g, \epsilon)$ where F is any of the many functions of (g, ϵ) for which $g \to 0$ exponentially as $(a - \eta) \to \infty$.

With this description of g, the differential equation for f becomes

$$(1 - h)h''' + \frac{h'h''}{3} + h - \frac{1}{3}\tau h' = 0. \tag{A}$$

Equation (A) admits solutions which decay exponentially as $\tau \to \infty$, and a numerical evaluation of f is now in progress. A complete demonstration of the boundary layer description of ψ is essential to the consistency of the inertial theory, although the actual structure of the jet is certainly influenced strongly by turbulent processes.

G. F. Carrier and A. R. Robinson, May, 1962

Editor's Notes: A discussion of inertial boundary currents in variable density ocean models

EDITOR'S NOTES: *A Discussion of Inertial Boundary Currents in Variable Density Ocean Models*

1. *The Effects of Upwelling and Stratification*

The foregoing papers have demonstrated the influence of singular regions of high relative vorticity on the determination of the horizontal circulation pattern everywhere in the ocean. For, although the east-west component of transport be geostrophic almost everywhere, it is not determined by a consideration of the geostrophic region alone. The Sverdrup vorticity balance determines only the north-south component of transport.

The detailed momentum balance which obtains in the geostrophic component of flow in the coastal currents is felt throughout the ocean. This is demonstrated by the striking difference between the single-cell pattern of a model closed by laminar-like friction and the double-cell pattern of a homogeneous model closed primarily by inertia. This result is in direct contradiction to the idea that geostrophy and mass conservation alone suffice to determine qualitative flow patterns (Stommel, 1958, page 154).

To understand even the gross features of large-scale circulations must involve a detailed consideration of all relevant processes which may occur in ageostrophic regions. In particular, if it can be demonstrated that the turbulent transfers of momentum and vorticity are of primary importance somewhere for the determination of the geostrophic flow everywhere, then a realistic treatment of the turbulent Reynolds-stresses is necessary. The behavior of the boundary layer equations is too sensitive to the form of a diffusive term to allow the use of constant eddy viscosity, even for qualitative results. There is, in fact, some evidence that the turbulent transfer of momentum takes place against the mean momentum gradient in the Gulf Stream region (Webster, 1961).

On the other hand, the inertial theory developed in the last four papers explores patterns of horizontal circulation which are closed by the nonlinear interaction of the mean field with itself rather than by correlated fluctuations. Although studies have been made of inertial boundary currents in oceans of variable density, complete circulation patterns closed primarily by inertia have been explored only in homogeneous ocean models. In this note the effects on the geostrophic flow in the interior ocean of upwelling and stratification in ageostrophic coastal regions are discussed. It will be shown that although the results for a two-layer model do not differ significantly from those for a homogeneous ocean, the results for an ocean of continuously variable density may. Two questions are posed. Can a western boundary current continue northward beyond the latitude of maximum wind-stress curl? Can an eastward geostrophic drift exist in a bounded ocean closed by inertial coastal currents?

2. *The Two-Layer Model*

The general equations appropriate to a two-layer coastal current (see the papers of Charney or Morgan) are geostrophic in the downstream direction, and inertial in the cross-stream direction. Let x be eastward, y be northward, g' be reduced gravity, and $D(x, y)$ be the depth of the lighter, upper layer in which all motion occurs. The Coriolis parameter is taken as $f = f_0 + \beta y$. Then

$$-fv + g'D_x = 0 \tag{1}$$

$$uv_x + vv_y + fu + g'D_y = 0 \tag{2}$$

$$(uD)_x + (vD)_y = 0 \tag{3}$$

express momentum and mass conservation. Here u, v are the horizontal velocity components, both of which are independent of depth because the flow is geostrophic in one direction. The components of horizontal mass transport are derivable from a stream function, specifically, $uD = -\psi_y$, $vD = \psi_x$. The vorticity equation which obtains from (1) and (2)

$$u(v_x + f)_x + v(v_x + f)_y + (u_x + v_y)(f + v_x) = 0 \tag{4}$$

may be integrated by using (3) to give

$$v_x + f = DP(\psi) \tag{5}$$

(the conservation of potential vorticity).

The initial stimulation for the investigation of inertial models of the wind-driven circulation lay in the suggestively accurate description of a Gulf Stream velocity profile which Stommel obtained by the application of equation (5) in its simplest form (Deacon *et al.*, 1955). In Stommel's model the potential vorticity has the same value on all streamlines, that is, $P(\psi) = c$, a constant. At all latitudes the deep layer is brought to the surface at the longitude $x = 0$; thus

$$v = \left(\frac{g'f}{c}\right)^{1/2} e^{-\xi}, \qquad D = \frac{f}{c}(1 - e^{-\xi}), \qquad \xi = \left(\frac{cf}{g'}\right)^{1/2} x. \qquad (6)$$

Comparison with the observed profile is shown in Figure 1. The agreement is good except for the shoreward edge of the stream. The more general treatment of the function $P(\psi)$ as made by Charney and Morgan has been seen to yield improved agreement.

A significant result of two-layer models is the separation phenomenon associated with the possibility of the deep layer coming to the surface at the western coast as the stream progresses northward and increases in transport. It is of particular interest to relate this phenomenon to the separation mechanism of the Carrier-Robinson homogeneous inertial model, according to which the stream cannot proceed beyond the latitude of maximum wind-stress curl. Morgan noted that the deep layer could come to the surface to the north of the region he considered; Charney assumed it to do so at the prescribed latitude of maximum transport.

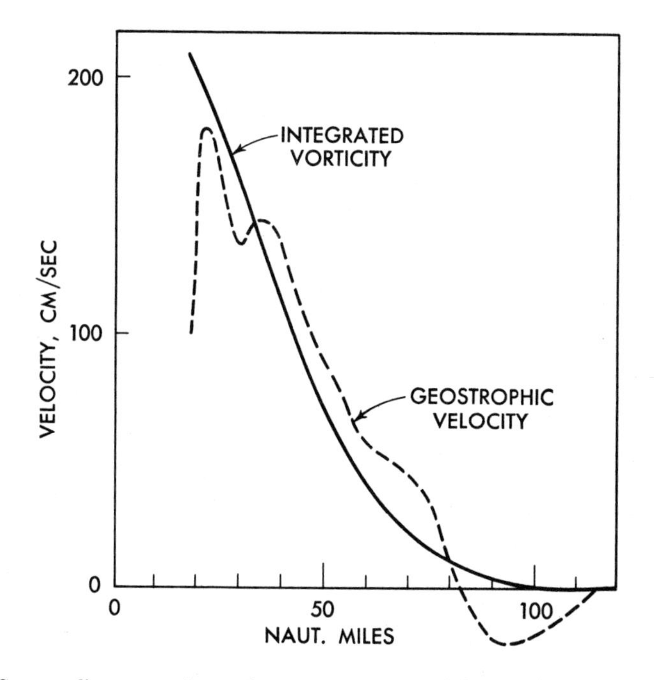

Fig. 1. Stommel's comparison of a constant potential vorticity model with Gulf Stream observations (*after* Deacon *et al.*, 1955).

We discuss both separation processes by considering the western current to form and flow above the latitude of zero wind-stress curl ($y = 0$). On the seaward side of the boundary current, the transport stream function for the interior $\psi_I(0, y) = \phi(y)$ yields a longitudinal transport given by $-\phi_y$. Let the depth of the warm layer be $h(y)$ along the coast and $H(y)$ at the seaward edge of the boundary layer where the longitudinal flow is $U(y)$. Under the usual assumption that ψ_I is proportional to the wind-stress curl (the latitudinal gradient of the stress from purely longitudinal winds) the latitude of maximum curl (y_M) corresponds to $U(y_M) = 0$. The two-layer separation mechanism may be derived most simply by two integrations. The geostrophic equation (1) is integrated across the boundary layer; the momentum equation (2) is partially integrated northward from $y = 0$ along the seaward edge of the boundary layer (where it expresses a geostrophic balance between interior quantities). Thus

$$h^2 - H^2 + \frac{2f}{g'}\phi = 0$$

and

$$H^2 - H^2_0 - \frac{2f}{g'}\phi + \frac{2\beta}{g'}\int_0^y \phi(y')dy' = 0$$

whence

$$h^2 = H^2_0 - \frac{2\beta}{g'}\int_0^y \phi\, dy', \tag{7}$$

where $H_0 = H(0) = h(0)$. For a given rate of transport into the coastal region, h may vanish at some latitude if the warm layer is not sufficiently deep at the southern boundary. H_0 is of course an external parameter in any purely wind-driven ocean model and is related to the total amount of warm water involved in the circulation.

The two-layer counterpart of the homogeneous ocean separation mechanism is not independent of the inertial nature of the stream as is the above mechanism. A demonstration of the nonlinear phenomenon has not been achieved by exact integration, but it may be exhibited succinctly by an examination of the asymptotic behavior of the boundary layer equations as they approach the geostrophic interior. We introduce the deviation of boundary-layer quantities from their interior values $\mu(x, y) = u(x, y) - U$, $\delta(x, y) = D(x, y) - H(y)$, where $U = -g'/fH_y$ by interior geostrophy. Since μ, v, $\delta \to 0$

as $x \to \infty$, the equations may be linearized at the edge of the boundary layer. In particular the continuity equation (3) becomes

$$H(\mu_x + \nu_y) + U\delta_x + H_y\nu = 0,$$

but since (1) implies $\delta_x = f\nu g'$, $\mu_x + \nu_y = 0$. The vorticity equation (4) now becomes

$$Uv_{xx} + \beta v = 0 \tag{8}$$

which is identical in form to the homogeneous ocean case. Thus boundary layers can exist only for $U < 0$ (westward geostrophic drift). The width of the layer is characterized by the length $\sqrt{-\beta/U(y)}$. As $|U|$ decreases northward the boundary current narrows and accelerates; separation must occur at $U = -\phi_y = 0$ (the latitude of maximum wind-stress curl under our assumptions). The symmetry of (4) with respect to the sign of x leads immediately to results for an eastern coast.

The condition $U < 0$ operating on a two-layer inertial model may be seen to result in the same qualitative patterns of horizontal circulation as those discussed by Carrier and Robinson for the homogeneous ocean. There must, however, be sufficient warm water in the upper layer so that the transport separation mechanism inherent in (7) does not operate to the south of $y = y_M$. Although separation will always occur at a latitude of maximum transport, it is not necessarily accompanied by $h = 0$ as required by Charney. If one associates a two-layer model with, the North Atlantic, for example, one is unable to distinguish empirically between the two mechanisms (see Charney, page 737; if one uses 900m for his $\bar{h}_0$, $\bar{h}_{\text{coast}} \neq 0$). Whether this is coincidental or significant can only be discussed in terms of an ocean model in which both wind-stress and thermohaline driving mechanisms are present, so that the amount of warm water which circulates is determined rather than parameterized.

It is of some interest to re-examine the case of constant potential vorticity in the present terms. Stommel's original example, equation (6), yields by (2) a longitudinal velocity field

$$u = \frac{u_\infty}{2} \frac{[(1 - \xi)e^{-2\xi} + e^{-\xi}(\xi - 2) + 2]}{(1 - e^{-\xi})}, \qquad u_\infty = -\frac{\beta g'}{fc}, \tag{9}$$

Since $\sqrt{cf/g'}$ must be real, $c > 0$ and $u < 0$ everywhere. In fact $|u|$ increases monotonically coastward across the stream; $u \to u_\infty/2\xi$ as $\xi \to 0$. The longitudinal transport field, however, is decreased coastward by this type of flow. Since near the origin $D \to (f/c)\xi$ there is a finite transport at $\xi = 0$ which at every latitude has half the value of the transport into the stream from the interior ocean. This difficulty is not however associated with the assumption of constant potential vorticity, but merely with the boundary condition applied. Setting $u(0, y) = v(x, 0) = 0$ but retaining $P(\psi) = c$ we have

$$D = \frac{f}{c}\left\{\left[\sqrt{\left(\frac{2f_0}{f} - 1\right)} - 1\right]\exp\left(-\sqrt{\frac{cf'}{g'}}\,x\right) + 1\right\}. \quad (10)$$

Since $v_x(0) \neq -f$, the longitudinal flow is well behaved. The solution (10) exhibits the requirement for interior westward drift ($c > 0$) and the two-layer separation mechanism (at $f = 2f_0$). The assumption of constant potential vorticity corresponds to a special case of an interior transport $UH = -\phi_y$ which is independent of latitude (Morgan's simple wind-system). Morgan's generalization is to allow a free variation of $D(x, 0) = H(0)$; that is, $H^2 = f^2/c^2 + c_1$ (c_1 a constant) generates Morgan's solutions and $c_1 = 0$ yields $P(\psi) = c$.

3. *A Continuously Variable Density Field*

In a two-layer model the density field at each latitude and longitude has but one degree of freedom. This imposes a strong coupling between the vertical and horizontal density gradients which has no *a priori* physical basis. The processes of stable stratification and thermal-wind shear become indistinguishable. Furthermore in the above model the assumption has been made that only the upper layer is in motion (no barotropic mode). In a three-dimensional model with a continuously variable vertical coordinate z, the above restrictions may be simultaneously relaxed. In such a model, however, the advantage of integration over vertical stresses is lost. We conceive of an interior ocean region in which the vertical stress is confined to a surface Ekman-layer. The distribution of vertical mass-flux at the lower edge of the layer (which is determined by the surface wind-stress gradients) drives the interior region (Stommel, 1958, Chapter 11).

We introduce a nondimensional density anomaly, s, by $\rho = \rho_0(1 - s)$ and assume that the density flux does not diverge in the coastal boundary layer. Then, under the Boussinesq approximation, equations (1) through (3) are replaced by the equations

$$-fv + \frac{1}{\rho_0}p_x = 0 \quad (11)$$

$$uv_x + vv_y + wv_z + fu + \frac{1}{\rho_0} p_y = 0 \tag{12}$$

$$-sg + \frac{1}{\rho_0} p_z = 0 \tag{13}$$

$$u_x + v_y + w_z = 0 \tag{14}$$

$$us_x + vs_y + ws_z = 0. \tag{15}$$

The bottom and surface are taken at two constant values of $z = \pm z_0/2$. We associate the upwelling mechanism with a large amplitude w occurring in (14) to combine with v in balancing the large $\partial u/\partial x$ necessary for a boundary current which conserves mass over the ocean basin ($\partial/\partial y$ and $\partial/\partial z$ assumed to remain of geometric scale). To isolate the upwelling mechanism from the effect of extremely large stresses in the surface Ekman-layer locally, we shall apply as boundary conditions $w(\pm z_0/2) = 0$. Since in the cases of interest the upwelling velocity will be much greater than the interior vertical velocity associated with the Ekman-layer divergence, we are merely assuming that the local atmospheric wind stresses are not imposed by the ocean.

In order to obtain conditions on the interior flow necessary for the existence of a three-dimensional inertial boundary layer an asymptotic expansion will again be made. In such an approximation the continuum counterpart of the two-layer separation mechanism may be expected to be lost. At the seaward edge of the current we assume two (independent) constant density gradients, $s_y = \Gamma$, $s_z = S$. The normal flow component will then have a linear dependence on height but an arbitrary dependence on latitude. Linearization is made in μ, v, w, σ, where

$$\sigma = s - (\Gamma y + Sz),\ \mu = u - U(y, z) = u - U_0(y) + \frac{g\Gamma z}{f}. \tag{16}$$

The asymptotic vorticity equation for v

$$U\left(v_{xx} + \frac{f^2}{sg} v_{zz}\right) + \beta v = 0 \tag{17}$$

exhibits an upwelling term. The vertical velocity is expressed by the coastal stream as

$$w = -\frac{1}{s}\left[\frac{Uf}{g} v_z + \Gamma v\right]. \tag{18}$$

The relatively simple form of (17) in which the y-dependence enters only parametrically and in which the coefficients are independent of x allows the analysis to be reduced to an eigenvalue problem for a second-order ordinary differential operator (confluent hypergeometric under (16)). Let

$$v = \nu(\zeta) \exp\left(\sqrt{\frac{sgh^2}{f^2}}\,\lambda x\right), \qquad \zeta = \frac{z}{z_0} \tag{19}$$

be substituted in (17) and (18). The result is

$$(1 + \alpha\zeta)\nu'' + [(1 + \alpha\zeta)\lambda^2 + \beta^*]\nu = 0 \tag{20}$$

with

$$\alpha(y) = -\frac{g\Gamma z_0}{fU_0(y)}, \qquad \beta^*(y) = \frac{\beta S g z_0^2}{U_0 f^2},$$

and the boundary conditions

$$(1 + \alpha\zeta)\nu' - \alpha\nu = 0 \text{ at } \zeta = \pm\tfrac{1}{2}. \tag{21}$$

The parameter α represents the effect of shear; β^* measures the influence of variable rotation in a boundary layer whose width has been scaled by the radius of deformation (appropriate to the stratified, rotating fluid). The condition that an inertial boundary layer exists is that the eigenvalue spectrum $\lambda(\alpha, \beta^*)$ be real. In general, the entire spectrum will be necessary to join the asymptotic approximation to the solution inshore.

The behavior of (20) and (21) in certain limiting cases is of interest. First let $\beta^* = 0$ (constant rotation). Then the coastal stream is an harmonic function $\nu = a_1 \cos(\lambda\zeta) + a_2 \sin(\lambda\zeta)$ and (21) yields

$$\alpha^2 \frac{\lambda}{2} \tan\left(\frac{\lambda}{2}\right)^2 + 4\left[\left(\frac{\lambda}{2}\right)^2\left(1 - \frac{\alpha^2}{4}\right) + \frac{\alpha^2}{4}\right] \tan\frac{\lambda}{2} - \frac{\lambda}{2}\alpha^2 = 0$$

for the eigenvalues. Three cases have been considered, $\alpha \to \infty$, $\alpha \to 0$ and $\alpha = \pm 2$, corresponding respectively to vanishing of the incoming flow at the center of the fluid region considered, far outside, and at either boundary. In all cases real eigenvalues exist. Thus Morgan's conclusion that the β-effect is essential for the existence of a coastal boundary layer (Morgan's equation (8.11) ff; see also equation (8) above) does not generalize to a more realistic case of variable density.

Now at the seaward edge we let the shear vanish but maintain stratification, $\alpha = 0$, $\beta^* \neq 0$. In this case ν is again harmonic but of argument $\sqrt{\lambda^2 + \beta^*}$. Upon application of the boundary conditions

(21) in its simplified form $\nu'(\pm 1/2) = 0$, a Fourier representation for $\nu(\zeta)$ may be chosen. However, any representation which forms a complete set (for the expansion at some x_i of an inshore condition) must contain a constant term if there is a net transport of mass associated with the ν-field. The constant term has an associated eigenvalue, λ_0, which must satisfy $\lambda_0^2 + \beta^* = 0$. Then $\beta^* < 0$ which implies $U_0 < 0$ and a westward drift. Thus if an eastward drift can occur, it must occur with finite α and the eigenvalue problem must be treated in its most general form. We do not attempt this here, but note in passing that results of calculations on a somewhat different model indicate the possibility of some eastward-drift solutions. Physically, the role of α is to vary the stratification at the edge of the boundary current in such a way that an "effective" β occurs of opposite sign to that due to the earth's curvature alone. The most recent compilation of observed geostrophic transport in the North Pacific indicates unambiguously an eastward drift above the latitude of maximum curl (Reid, 1962).

In a solution in which an eastward geostrophic flow occurs in at least part of the northern half-basin, the role of the midlatitude jet (Carrier and Robinson, Section 3.2) in the over-all conservation of mass may no longer be simply inferred. A complete separation of the western boundary current may no longer occur; the nature of the singular region which begins at the latitude $U(y_M) = 0$ must be explored in terms of a detailed model. We may, however, inquire into the effect of finite α upon the singular region. As $U_0 \to 0$ both α and β^* grow large but their ratio $\alpha/\beta^* = \Gamma\pi/\beta S z_0 \equiv r$ remains finite. Equation (20) now has a singularity at $\zeta = 0$; in general the solution which is well behaved at the origin will be unable to satisfy the (symmetric) double condition imposed by (21) in this limit. Thus a singular behavior around $y = y_M$ is indicated for all values of r.

References

Deacon, G. E. R., H. U. Sverdrup, H. Stommel and C. W. Thornthwaite, 1955. Discussion on the relationships between meteorology and oceanography. *J. Mar. Res.* **14,** 499.

Ried, J. L., 1961. On the geostrophic flow at the surface of the Pacific Ocean with respect to the 1000-decibar surface. *Tellus* **13,** 489.

Stommel, H., 1958. *The Gulf Stream: a Physical and Dynamical Description.* University of California Press.

Webster, F., 1961. The effects of meanders on the kinetic energy balance of the Gulf Stream. *Tellus* **13,** 392.